How To Build Your
CABIN OR MODERN VACATION HOME

How To Build Your
CABIN OR
MODERN
VACATION
HOME

By
HARRY WALTON

POPULAR SCIENCE

HARPER & ROW
New York, Evanston, San Francisco, London

Library of Congress Catalog Card Number: 64-13134
ISBN: 0-06-014519-6

First Edition, 1964
Ten Printings

Second Edition, Revised and Updated, 1976

Second Printing, 1977

Manufactured in the United States of America

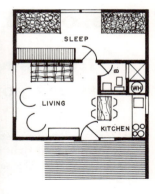

CONTENTS

Glossary of Building Terms   6

1. The Vacation Home Movement   13

2. Choosing the Site and Financing Construction   16

3. A Sampler of Modern Vacation Homes   23

4. Tools for Building Your Vacation Home   45

5. Locating and Building the Foundation   57

6. A Simple Pole Cabin and Carport   71

7. Building the True Log Cabin   79

8. Frame, Panel and Other Structures   95

9. Porches and Outside Walls   117

10. Fireplaces, Heaters and Chimneys   130

11. Finishing the Interior of Your Cabin   140

12. Modern Utilities for the Vacation Home   148

Where to Write for Further Information   157

Index   158

Before You Begin...

Here is a glossary of building terms you'll find in this book

ADZE   A long-handled cutting implement similar to an axe, but with the blade at right angles like that of a hoe.

AGGREGATE   The sand and gravel mixed with cement to make concrete.

AMPERE, AMPERAGE   A measure of electrical flow or quantity.

ANCHOR BOLTS   Bolts set into concrete to secure house sills, railings or other members to the masonry.

ANGLE IRON   Structural iron in the form of a right-angled bar; also small right-angled mending brackets.

APRON   A horizontal wooden member placed with its face vertical under a window sill, workbench top or built-in.

ARMORED CABLE   Electrical conductors housed in a spiral-wound outer shield or armor.

ARRIS   The sharp corner formed wherever two surfaces meet, for example between one edge and one face of a board.

BACKFILL   To return earth to the place from which it was removed, as for example against a foundation wall.

BALLOON FRAMING   House framing in which studs and corner posts are continuous from sill to rafter plate.

BASEBOARD   A board or molding applied to the bottom of a wall to conceal the gap between wall covering and floor.

BATTENS   Wood strips or light boards used to cover joints or gaps between other members.

BATTER BOARDS   Horizontal boards supporting guide lines for laying out foundation perimeters.

BEAD, BEADING   Molding with a semicircular cross section, smaller than half-round molding.

BEAM   A heavy load-bearing timber installed horizontally.

BEARING WALL   A wall that supports part of the upper-floor and roof load.

BEVEL   An angle other than a right angle; an edge cut at less than 90 degrees, most commonly at 45 degrees.

BEVEL SIDING   Boards with a wedgelike cross section, installed with the thick lower edge of one overlapping the thinner upper edge of the one below.

BOARD FOOT   A measure of lumber, nominally a 1′ by 1′ piece of 1″ stock or its cubic equivalent. Thus an 8′ length of 2-by-6 is charged for as 8 board feet; a 12′ length of 1-by-6 as 6 board feet.

BOX SILL   A type of floor framing in which the ends of the joists are enclosed by header joists.

ARRIS

BEVEL

BRACE A member nailed to other members to hold them rigidly in position, usually by forming a triangle with them.

BRAD A light, small-headed nail.

BRIDGING Solid pieces or diagonal bracing nailed between joists to keep them from twisting under floor loads.

BUTT JOINT A simple joint made by abutting one member against another, end to end, end to edge, or edge to edge.

BX CABLE Same as armored cable.

CASING Molding or boards applied around window and door openings as trim.

CHAMFER

CHAMFER A bevel on part of an edge only.

CLAPBOARD A type of siding, similar to bevel siding.

CLINCH To bend over the exposed sharp end of a nail after it has penetrated the work.

CLINCH

COLLAR BEAM A horizontal member spanning two opposite rafters, above their lower ends, tying them together and forming in effect a truss.

COMPOSITION BOARD Synthetic panel material, made by compressing wood fibers into sheets.

CORNICE The projecting top of a wall, or the molding applied there.

COURSE A horizontal line or layer of brick, shingles, stone, siding or other material applied in increments.

COVE A concave shape; molding with all or part of its face having a concave cross section.

CROWN An upward arching or convex shape, such as the crown of a road or other surface that insures drainage; a type of molding having a convex cross section.

DADO

DADO, DADO JOINT A square-cut, flat-bottomed groove, usually across the grain; a joint made by fitting another member into such a groove.

DIAGONAL SHEATHING Sheathing boards applied to studs at an angle, usually 45 degrees, to provide a bracing effect and form a more rigid wall.

DOWEL, DOWEL PIN Hardwood in the shape of a round rod; a pin cut from a dowel, or a steel pin, used to join and align two members.

DOUBLED HEADER The horizontal member across the top of a window or door opening, or nailed across the ends of the joists in a stair well or chimney opening. Usually such headers consist of two pieces of stock, hence are doubled.

DOUBLE-HUNG WINDOW A window consisting of two sash that slide vertically.

DRIP CAP A molding or other projecting member that allows water to drip off instead of penetrating.

DROP SIDING Siding boards milled with a rabbet or a groove that fits over thinner tongue or edge on the board below.

DRY WALL An interior wall covered with plywood, composition board, ordinary boards or paneling instead of wet-mixed plaster or stucco.

DRY WELL   A hole in the ground, lined and filled with coarse gravel or stone, to which waste water is conducted so as to dissipate into the subsoil below.

DUTCH DOOR   A door consisting of separately hinged halves, which may be opened and closed separately.

EAVES   That part of a roof which overhangs the walls.

EDGE   Either of the two narrower longitudinal surfaces of a piece of sawed lumber.

EXPANSION JOINT   A gap left in cast concrete and filled with calking or other compressible material to allow the masonry to expand without cracking or heaving.

FACE   Either of the two wider longitudinal surfaces of a piece of sawed lumber.

FACE-NAIL   To nail a piece through the face.

FILLER   A paste, sometimes colored to match wood finishes, used to fill coarse or open-pored grain in some woods before other finishes are applied.

FIRE BRICK   Special bricks that withstand heat without cracking.

FIRE STOPS   Pieces of wood installed between studs to close the chimney-like channel between them and thus slow the spread of fire through a wall.

FISH JOINT   A butt joint reinforced by scabs or plates on one or both sides.

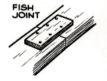

FLASHING   Sheet metal or other material laid to bridge the joints between a roof and a chimney or other parts of a structure and so keep water from entering.

FLUE   The passageway in a chimney through which combustion gases pass out.

FLUSH, FLUSH JOINT   The alignment of two surfaces in a common plane, so that neither projects.

FOOTING   The heaviest part of a foundation, that which rests directly on the subsoil.

FORM   A wooden or other enclosure into which concrete is poured, which gives it its shape.

FOUNDATION   That part of a structure on which the framing rests, usually masonry.

FRAMING   The skeleton of a house, a built-in, or a piece of furniture that gives it its shape and bears its weight.

FURRING   Wooden or metal strips installed to provide a nailing base or an all-over plane surface for following material.

GABLE   The triangular end of a sloped roof.

GAIN   A shallow notch cut to accommodate a hinge.

GALVANIZED   Zinc-coated to resist rust.

GIRDER   A horizontally placed timber, either solid or built up of smaller members, used to support a load over an opening or between foundation piers.

GIRT   A horizontal piece nailed between or across vertical members such as studs to reinforce them, provide a nailing base, or support other members.

GRADE   The ground level or street-curb height; the ground slope.

driven into a hole in plaster or masonry and will expand when a nail, screw or bolt is driven into it, so anchoring the screw or other fastening.

SECTION, SECTIONAL VIEW A drawing that shows a subject as though it were cut through and the cut portion exposed.

SHAKES A type of wooden wall covering similar to shingles but larger and of a standard size (6″ by 36″).

SHEATHING Boards or panels applied to the outside of wall studs or rafters for greater weather tightness, to brace the framing, and as a nailing base for shingles, siding or other covering.

SHEATHING PAPER Building paper applied outside sheathing to keep out rain and wind.

SHED ROOF

SHED ROOF A pitched roof sloping only one way.

SHIM A piece of material inserted behind or under another to raise, level, or bring it flush with another.

SHINGLES A type of roof and wall covering, originally wedge-shaped pieces of wood in certain standard lengths but random widths, which are applied in overlapping patterns. Also simulated shingles made of asphalt or asbestos composition material in both individual and strip form.

SHIPLAP A from of bevel siding with a rabbet in the thick edge that overlaps the thinner upper edge of the board below.

SIDING The weathertight outside covering of exterior walls.

SILL The undermost wooden member of house framing, which rests directly on the masonry foundation. The bottom member of a door or window opening.

SILL BOLT An anchor bolt holding a sill.

SMOKE CHAMBER The cavity above the throat of a fireplace.

SOFFIT

SOFFIT A horizontal panel enclosing an underside part of a structure, such as the eaves overhang.

SOIL PIPE Cast-iron pipe used for sewer and waste lines.

SOLE PLATE The horizontal member on which wall studs rest.

SPACER A piece inserted to keep others apart, and so to maintain a desired spacing.

SPAN The horizontal distance bridged by a truss, girder, beam or roof.

STIRRUP Same as Hanger.

STRAIGHTEDGE A ruler; a board selected for straightness as a guide in marking or aligning work.

STRINGER One of the two side members of a stair structure that support the treads and risers.

SQUARE At precisely 90 degrees, or right angles; also a right-angled tool for marking out or testing squareness.

STUD, STUDDING A vertical framing member of a wall; the series of studs that frame a wall.

SUBFLOOR Rough boards or plywood nailed directly to the joists as a base for the finish floor.

TENON A tongue or projection shaped to fit into a mortise.

THICKNESS The measurement across an edge of a board.

TIE BEAM A horizontal member nailed across the bottom ends

NONBEARING WALL or PARTITION   A wall that divides an area but carries none of the structural load.

NOSING   That part of a stair tread which extends past the vertical riser.

ON CENTER (O.C.)   A measure of spacing taken from the center of one member to the center of the next.

OUT OF PLUMB   Not plumb or truly vertical.

PARTING STRIP   A thin protruding strip that divides the two channels in which the upper and lower sash of a double-hung window slide.

PENNY (d)   The standard unit of nail size.

PIERS   Individual masonry supports, in the form of blocks, pyramids or columns.

PITCH   The slope of a roof, a floor, a line of pipe or the ground.

PLATE   That horizontal member atop a wall on which the rafters rest. See also SOLE PLATE.

PLATFORM FRAMING   House framing in which the sole plate rests on the subfloor and not on the sill.

PLUMB   Precisely vertical, at right angles to the horizontal.

PLUMB BOB   The weight on a plumb line.

PLUMB LINE   A cord having a pointed weight fastened to one end; hanging at rest, it indicates a true vertical.

PLY   One of the layers of which laminated material such as building paper, some insulation, felt and plywood is made.

PURLIN   A horizontal member supported under rafters to reinforce them against roof loads.

QUARTER-ROUND   Molding with the cross section of one quarter of a circular area.

QUARTER ROUND

RABBET   A right-angled notch cut into an edge or end, or one formed by nailing on a ledger strip.

RABBET

RABBET JOINT   A joint made by fitting all or part of one piece into a rabbet cut in the other.

RAFTER   One of the members that frame a roof and support the roof covering.

RIDGE CAP   A continuous piece of wood or metal fitted over roof covering at the peak to keep out water.

RABBET JOINT

RIDGEPOLE, RIDGE PIECE   The longitudinal member that forms the peak of a roof, on which the rafters are butted.

RISE   The difference in height between successive stair treads; the height difference between the plate and ridge ends of a rafter.

RISER   The vertical board under a stair tread.

RISER

RUN   The horizontal distance between the top and bottom of stairs; the horizontal distance between the plate and ridge ends of a rafter.

SADDLE   A shaped board fitted under a door; a curved shape or fillet built between a roof and a chimney to support flashing.

SASH   The wooden frame in which window glass is mounted; also the complete unit with the glass.

SCAB   A piece fastened across a joint to reinforce it; a board nailed to the buried part of a post to help it resist side thrust.

SCAB

SCREW ANCHOR   A fiber, lead or plastic bushing that may be

GRADING   Altering the lay of the ground by excavating, filling or otherwise moving earth.

GROOVE   A channel running lengthwise of a piece of wood, or with the grain.

GROUT   A thin mixture of cement and sand; thin cement mortar.

GUSSET   A triangular reinforcing plate used to join members at an angle.

HALF-ROUND   Molding with a semicircular cross section.

HANGER   A metal bracket or stirrup nailed to one member to hold another at right angles to it.

HARDBOARD   A grainless composition board made of compressed wood fibers and somewhat harder than most woods.

HEADER   A horizontal member, often doubled, placed across studs or joists to frame an opening.

HIP ROOF

HIP RAFTER   A rafter framing an outside angle of a roof.

HIP ROOF   A pyramid-like roof that slopes four ways.

I-BEAM   A structural steel member with the cross section of the letter I.

JACK RAFTER   A rafter shorter than others, used in framing intersecting roof slopes.

JAMB   The inner side lining of a door or window frame.

JOINT   The mating surfaces or fit between two members; also to plane or dress wood flat, square, and straight.

LAP JOINT

JOIST   One of the horizontal beams that frame a floor or ceiling.

JOIST HANGER   A metal fitting used to fasten joists to girders or headers at the same level.

LAG SCREW   A big, heavy-duty wood screw with a square head.

LAP JOINT   A joint made by overlapping parts of two members.

LATH   Thin wood strips nailed across studs as a backing for wall plaster; wire mesh for the same purpose.

LATTICE   A criss-cross arrangement of lath, furring strips or other light lumber installed to admit air but exclude birds and rodents.

LEDGER STRIP   A strip nailed to a wider member to form a step or rabbet on which a third piece may rest.

LEDGER STRIP

LEVEL   Precisely horizontal; an instrument in which fluid in glass tubes indicates level alignment.

LINTEL   Same as Header.

LOAD-BEARING WALL   Same as Bearing Wall.

LOUVER   An arrangement of slats so sloped as to shed rain but admit air.

MITER JOINT

MITER, MITER JOINT   To cut the ends of two members at 45 degrees; a 90-degree joint made by joining two such pieces.

MOLDING   Wood strips milled to various cross-sectional contours, or similar extruded metal strips.

MORTAR   A wet mixture of sand, cement and sometimes lime, used as a bonding agent for brick or stone work.

MORTISE

TENON

MORTISE   A hole or socket cut in one member to receive all or part of another; an opening made to house a lock mechanism. See TENON.

of opposite rafters to tie them and the wall plates together.

TOENAIL   To nail through one surface of a member at such an angle that the nail emerges from another to penetrate a second member butted against the first.

TONGUE AND GROOVE   Milled lumber having a groove in one edge and a matching tongue on the other, those of successive pieces fitting together.

TREAD   The horizontal, load-carrying part of a stair step.

TRIM   Finish molding or other material applied for appearance.

TRIMMER   An extra joist or stud to which the header is nailed in framing an opening.

VALLEY   The inside angle formed by intersecting gable roofs.

VENEER   A thin layer, usually of more costly wood, glued to cheaper wood or metal for appearance.

VITRIFIED PIPE   Clay pipe that has been baked to a hard glaze.

WAINSCOTING   Paneling that covers only a lower part of an interior wall.

WALL BOARD   Synthetic panels of hardboard, fiber, gypsum, asbestos, plywood, cardboard or other material.

WET WALL   An interior wall covered with plaster or stucco, which must be applied wet.

WIDTH   The measurement across a face of a board.

CHAPTER ONE

THE VACATION HOME MOVEMENT

BESIDES A second bathroom, a second telephone and a second car, many American families either own or are planning to acquire a second home away from home. The best recent estimates suggest that there are already well over a million cabins, lodges, and other leisure-time dwellings in this country. Some authorities believe there will be twice that many in a few years. One of them may well be yours.

There are sound reasons for both the present boom and a big future increase. Shorter working hours give people more leisure time. Family incomes are rising. We are more aware of a need for wholesome recreation than ever before. The vacation home is an excellent locale for entertaining, and many people enjoy the distinction of owning one.

The expanding highway program is constantly opening new vacation territory. As the network of high-speed, divided roads grows, you will be able to drive to many areas once too far from city and suburban centers for convenient second-home commuting. Wherever you live, some suitable land is probably within automobile distance. A country rich in lakes offers water sports far from its coast lines. Rivers and woods tempt the sportsman. Even the desert blossoms with leisure homes. A beach site affords swimming, boating, fishing and lazy hours of relaxation by the sea.

From the family standpoint, a vacation home should mean a new and better concept of living. It promises years of enjoyment for all. With its shelter and sports equipment ready and waiting, a family can often take impromptu weekend vacations, free of the necessity of making reservations in advance and doing much packing or hauling.

Having your own place also permits more orderly planning, never frustrated by a lack of resort space on vacation dates. Yet flexibility remains; you can change dates any time without losing reservations or deposits. In the long run, provided you don't overextend yourself financially, a second home should save you money over the usual cost of resort vacations.

If you do a canny job of locating and building, the financial aspect may

13

be improved by renting out your vacation home part of the time. Related families sometimes share the building and carrying cost of a leisure home, using it on a rotation basis. Of course either arrangement costs you some of the flexibility in planning (or rather not-planning) your own occupancy, but may make dollars and sense. Vacation rentals are high, and some fortunate owners make enough money from them to cover most of the property's yearly costs.

If you are a cliff dweller, preferring apartment convenience for routine living, a vacation home may be all the more indicated. It could afford a wonderful change of pace, lift you out of city canyons into open country as often—or as seldom—as you please, broaden your outlook, and still leave you the convenience of a city residence for day-to-day affairs.

Although plenty of young families are buying or building leisure homes on modest incomes (the big demand, reports the National Association of Home Builders, comes from those in the $6,000 to $10,000 income group), older folk buy them as retirement homes. In addition, some middle-aged people buy a vacation home that can become their retirement home later on. When they do retire, the property should be clear of indebtedness, leaving only taxes and upkeep to pay out of reduced income. This idea is becoming increasingly popular. However, a vacation-and-retirement home does have some special requirements, to be considered in a later chapter.

Building your own vacation home, whether from the ground up or by finishing a "shell" structure, can be an absorbing adventure and an exciting change from your regular work. Prerequisites for this, to be sure, are some knowledge of common tool techniques and a liking for working with your hands. Tackled with enthusiasm, the problems encountered can usually be taken in stride. Many an amateur builder finds that he works harder, sleeps more soundly, feels better than ever before in his life—and thoroughly enjoys the experience.

If you're a quick and skillful builder, you may be able to sell your vacation home at a profit and build another—perhaps better—home with the proceeds. This rosy prospect must be tempered with a word of caution. Cash profits are subject to income tax, and you may find it difficult to list your own labors as a deduction. Also, the place must be located and built with canny foresight and an awareness of local market values. Unless you have the time and inclination to inform yourself, it is easy to wind up with a loss.

Today's vacation homes range from modest hunting and fishing cabins to fresh, startling designs with picture windows, terraces and sun decks. Released from the conventions of urban and suburban building, architects have produced interesting cantilever, A-frame, chalet and breezeway structures. Many are planned so that the outdoors becomes part of the decor. New materials in some cases help create the design.

In this book are leisure-home plans for various tastes, as well as directions for building them, for providing utilities and for finishing interiors. Logs, the building material of our early settlers, still make durable structures that blend admirably with wooded terrain. How to build with logs, a mystery to many, is explained in a chapter on the log cabin. Another chapter describes modern materials that make building other types of vacation shelters easier and often speedier.

Of great help to the do-it-yourself builder is today's excellent assortment of portable power tools. Some of these reduce to minutes what would take hours of hand labor. With such tools, even a log cabin is easier to build than ever before. Chapter 4 shows the reader the most popular and useful of these tools.

Also included are sources from which you can get architects' plans other than those shown in this book, and government agencies to which you may apply to acquire government land for vacation-home sites.

CHAPTER TWO

CHOOSING THE SITE AND FINANCING CONSTRUCTION

IF THERE is one supremely important factor in planning your vacation home, it is its location. You can alter some house plans even after the walls are up, but you'll have to live with the site once the foundations are down. Take time to learn all you possibly can about a prospective site. Not only your cash investment, but your future enjoyment depends on choosing the right spot.

Of course, you will first consider whether the area has the sort of recreational facilities you want. For water sports, it must obviously be near a beach, lake or river. Swimming, boating and fishing are so popular that most people won't want a vacation home without them. Some successful leisure-home developers will not even consider land that doesn't have waterfront access. Resale of vacation property is certainly easier if it has water facilities.

There are exceptions, of course—the ski lodge and hunting cabin, for example. It's wise to buy land for these purposes in areas you know at first hand, for it may be hard to judge such sports potentialities out of season. Aside from these special cases, land with access to water is usually a better choice. Apart from your own enjoyment of water sports, they can keep children contented for hours and leave parents free to enjoy less strenuous pursuits.

The ideal vacation area may also offer golf courses, tennis and squash courts. Sometimes these are part of a development, sometimes under community auspices. The next important thing to consider about a vacation-home area is its distance from your year-around home. Is it near enough for weekend vacations, or so far away that only once-a-year trips will be feasible? Obviously you will get more use of your vacation home if it is within reasonable reach. For example, the family can live there all season while Dad joins it during weekends.

What is "too far," however, varies with the region and one's own evaluation. Many Westerners think nothing of driving 300 miles or more on a vacation jaunt, whereas people in more crowded areas, driving on crowded roads, may think half that as far as they care to go for brief stays. The age of young children is also a factor; tots tend to become restless after riding a couple of hours.

Although modern high-speed roads do cut travel time, be wary of counting on a highway that is still only a dotted line on the map. Road construction schedules are often optimistic; delays are common and often lengthy.

Developers of vacation land generally prefer locations within two hours' drive of year-around towns and suburbs, though some on the West Coast extend the limit to two and a half hours.

Is the area accessible the year around or only part of the time? Will soggy roads keep you out during the spring fishing season? Will roads be ploughed when you want to get there for skiing? Are there any other factors, physical or regulatory, to prevent you from reaching or occupying your leisure home part of the time? How's the climate? Does the area have excessive rainfall in the vacation months? What are seasonal temperatures? How many sunny days can you expect for enjoying the beach? Will there be enough snowfall for good skiing? Local weather bureaus and newspaper records are better sources of information on such points than word-of-mouth assurance.

The area's climate has a bearing not only on how much you can enjoy your vacation home, but on whether it will require insulation, heating equipment, or air conditioning. You cannot take it for granted that the climate will be the same as where you live, even if your all-year home is relatively near. A range of hills, the proximity of water, prevailing winds, even a small difference in elevation can alter climate enormously.

The retire-later leisure home should be in or near a year-around community rather than in a vacation area that is almost deserted half the year. Retired people rarely want to live in secluded locations. The house should be within reach of neighbors, and with near access to markets, theaters, medical facilities and other conveniences.

Is the community growing or declining? What will the area be like when you are ready to retire? Are temperature and rainfall moderate? A mild climate is not only kinder to older people, but saves them fuel in winter, air-conditioning costs in summer, which may count for much in a reduced retirement income.

CHOOSING A SITE. Once you have chosen an area, you are ready to look for a building site. Real-estate ads are one hunting ground; many appear in big-city newspapers, but don't ignore local ones. Local agents, chambers of commerce, building and loan associations, banks and lumber dealers may be able to suggest sites for you to consider.

Sometimes a land bargain can be obtained through the local tax assessor from the tax-delinquent list. If, on the other hand, you find a likely spot with no for-sale sign or owner identification, note its location as well as you can with reference to the nearest marked property, road or other landmark. With this, you can consult maps and records at the local county court house to find the owner.

Never buy sight unseen. Go to visit the site yourself, no matter how glow-ing the description. Nobody else can judge it quite from your own standpoint.

Once you've pinpointed a building spot—and especially if you've fallen in love with it—is the time to take a long second look, with special attention to the following:

Roads. Do they run all the way to the property, or must you build the last stretch? If so, at what cost? Will existing roads remain passable during spring rains and winter snowfalls? Are all bridges in, sound, and publicly main-tained?

Water. If there is a well or spring, get a report on the purity of its water from the local health department (which will require a sample). If there is no water supply, inspect neighboring sites and get estimates for providing one. Would it be possible to pipe water in at reasonable cost? Is there room enough to locate a septic tank or other sanitary facilities at least 100 feet from the well or spring?

Hazards. Is the site at the foot of high ground where it may be subject to flooding, or to rock or soil slides? Are there any big trees, rocks or overhangs that may fall on the site at some future time? Is there an escape route in case of forest fires? Will abnormally high tides or winds endanger a beach house at this spot? Is the soil too sandy or too marshy to afford a firm building foundation? Marshy ground near by suggests poor drainage, a high water table, and mosquito breeding grounds.

Orientation. Will your leisure home be in the eternal shadow of high hills, or overexposed to summer sun? Does the terrain cut off cooling breezes, or channel cold winds towards the house in chill or rainy weather? Will the site enable you to place the house advantageously, with the larger walls facing north and south rather than east and west, for best control of the sun's effects? Can the structure be oriented to take advantage of natural shade?

Utilities. Is electricity available? Must power poles be erected at your expense? You can of course do without electricity, but it may save disappoint-ment to find out whether you will have to. It makes a big difference, too, in your choice of power tools for building. Bottled gas can generally be used for cooking and light-duty heating.

Taxes and Assessments. What are they now, and how much will they in-crease as you add improvements? Are new bond issues, new schools or other community projects slated to increase taxes in the near future?

What to pay for the site depends on its location, desirability, recreation facilities and the cost of similar parcels near by. The actual price may be a matter of bargaining; most agents will accept a lower counteroffer if you back it with a deposit (the owner may of course refuse it, or come back with a compromise figure). Remember that land cost is only your first cost; the site is worth little to you until you build on it.

To decide what you can afford to pay demands cool financial judgment.

Usually it will depend upon your current income, what savings you can spare, and how long you plan to wait before building.

The reason for the latter is that you must, in most vacation areas, have clear title to the building plot before you can expect to find financing for the house. Prospective lenders expect you to have the site paid for before you seek construction funds.

THE LEGAL ASPECTS. Once you have found land you want to buy, at a price that is satisfactory, it's time to retain a lawyer to handle the legal matters. In some localities you'll find a lawyer referral service. If it's not listed in the phone book, ask the local bar association or legal aid society.

The first matter the lawyer should handle for you is the contract of sale. This is a form (signed by seller and buyer) that states what property is to be sold, by whom, and at what price. Next, a title search must be made, to ascertain whether the seller of the property actually owns it. Your lawyer will check the records, in the office of the town or county clerk, of sales of the property in the last fifty years. One object of the search is to determine if there are any claims against the property, such as liens for unpaid bills owed by some previous owner. The search should also reveal any easements that might have been granted long ago, permitting someone else to use the property for some purpose—for example, to drive through it to reach other property. If the title search reveals serious encumbrances on the property, you want to be able to cancel the deal without losing any money (such as a deposit). Your lawyer can draw up the contract of sale in such a way as to protect you. He can also guard against other pitfalls of which you, as a layman, may be unaware. Finally, he can draw up the deed to the property. Considering all that is involved, it is unwise to view the legal aspects of your land purchase as a do-it-yourself enterprise.

ZONING AND BUILDING CODES. Before you decide to buy any property, look into the local zoning and building codes. These can affect your building plans in many ways.

Zoning codes vary widely, often in different parts of the same community—even on opposite sides of the same road. Some merely specify the minimum area allowed for a building lot and the purpose for which it may be used. It's also likely that the setbacks from property lines will be specified. For instance, you may be required to build your house at least 50' back from the road, and you might not be permitted to build closer than 25' from the side and rear boundaries of your property. Such rules protect you in that they keep the houses far enough apart for privacy. But they may also have the effect of limiting the size of your house if your lot is a small one. Other zoning codes are more restrictive, in some cases even specifying the style of the house. In any event, be sure you know the local zoning regulations that cover your particular building site before you decide to buy.

Building codes deal with the structure of your house, usually specifying such details as joist and rafter sizes for different spans, stud spacing, and similar items. Usually, they also cover plumbing, wiring, and septic system requirements. As they serve as guides to good building practices, they are more often a help than a hindrance. If any part of the code isn't clear to you, ask the building inspector to clarify it for you. The chances are your work will have to be inspected before the house is approved for final occupancy, so be sure that all specifications in the code are followed correctly.

WELLS. Although in some outlying areas shallow dug wells are still used, a drilled deep well is a better choice because it is not as vulnerable to contamination by surface water. A deep well is not a do-it-yourself project, however, because of the costly specialized equipment required, so a professional well driller is called for. Look for well drillers in the yellow pages of the local phone book, and get prices from several. You need to know not only the price per foot of well depth, but the price per foot of "casing," the large pipe that will be installed down to where the well enters the rock layer. Also get a price on a well pump and related tank and piping, installed. Compare this with the cost of comparable equipment if you do your own installation work. Be sure to get a written contract for the well drilling, and be sure it covers all details, so you won't be surprised by unexpected extras. Well drillers can't give you an accurate advance estimate of the depth at which your well will strike water, as wells only a few yards apart may strike water at widely differing depths. The best you can do is ask other residents in the area about the depth of their wells, and hope yours won't be too much deeper.

FINANCING A VACATION HOME. Borrowing money for vacation-home construction is not as easy as financing a year-around house. The future-retirement house is a different matter, for it is usually in a settled community, completely finished, and equipped for year-around occupancy. These factors make it possible to get a conventional mortgage in many cases.

But the shelter intended only for vacation living is often in open country, of simple construction, and unsuited for year-around occupancy. Frequently it is merely a shell which the owner intends to finish as time and money permit. Until such a house is completed, lenders feel it has small mortgage value; an unfinished house would bring little in a foreclosure sale and therefore is considered poor security.

One way to finance the vacation home is to get a short-term (five to seven year) personal loan. Although the property may be pledged, lenders consider it only partial collateral. Your personal credit and other assets count for more, as such loans are essentially "character loans."

Another way to borrow construction money is to give a second mortgage on your year-around home. This is possible only if you have a fair-sized equity in it, that is, if you have reduced the amount of the mortgage considerably by payments. The equity must be at least equal to the amount you wish to borrow.

The risk here is that failure to make payments on the second mortgage could result in foreclosure on the more valuable permanent home. Unless payments on both mortgages will be well within your assured income, and you have some emergency funds besides, this kind of borrowing cannot be recommended.

Interest is usually high on leisure-home loans, for the same reason that ordinary mortgages are not readily available. If you are planning to buy a prefab or precut house or cabin, however, ask the supplier or manufacturer about financing. You may find there's a specially tailored plan available. It's wise, too, to check not only with local banks and lending institutions, but also with one or two outside the immediate area. If your vacation home will be winterized and equipped with central heating, it is usually easier to borrow for its construction, as it will have greater sales possibilities and is therefore considered better security.

Itemize the cost of all the building materials you'll require, if you plan to do your own building work. This not only lets you know in advance what you'll need to spend, but may also be very helpful in obtaining financing. Many banks and lending institutions are less than enthusiastic about lending money to a nonprofessional for home construction unless he has building experience or can show some indication of his ability to do the job. A clear construction plan and a detailed list of materials and costs may be required before a loan is even considered.

Base your figuring on prices in the general area—after shopping around. You are likely to find considerable price differences for the same items at different suppliers. When the financing has been arranged, and your construction job has reached the stage where plumbing fixtures and appliances are to be installed, by all means check into sources of used fixtures and appliances, such as building wreckers in nearby areas. You'll usually find them listed in the yellow pages under "Wrecking Contractors." Their wares range from used lumber and windows and doors to fixtures and appliances, sometimes at savings of 50 percent or more.

PAY AS YOU GO. If you plan to start small in an outlying area where you can build any type of house or cabin you want, without restriction, you may not need to borrow to cover building costs. This way, once the land is paid for, you may find you can afford to build a room at a time (if you plan for it) so that when you're through building you're through paying. No mortgage payments, no interest to add up. Many people have done it, using the first completed room as a camp-style headquarters to live in on weekends and vacations while building the rest of the house.

Depending on your income, you may have to borrow to pay for essential items like a deep well or a septic system, but the amounts involved are only a fraction of the total cost of the house, and can be paid off in a relatively short time. And, of course, septic systems are often built by the homeowner.

Mail-order houses selling plastic pipe and other plumbing materials can usually supply complete instructions for constructing a septic-tank drainage field. You can buy the tank locally. Look into the do-it-yourself septic system possibilities and decide whether you feel you could do the job. If you'd prefer to have it done for you, shop for the lowest price.

CHAPTER THREE

A SAMPLER OF MODERN VACATION HOMES

In this chapter you will find a sampling of vacation houses of various kinds. They range from conventional cottages and two-story structures to A-frames and waterside homes with attached boat houses. Construction costs vary almost as widely as the designs.

Well worth browsing over, these designs illustrate what can be done within the compass of a small-cubage house to achieve big-scale leisure living. Outdoor terraces or sun decks add greatly to this result. Most of these structures also show the profound influence of modern materials in building better leisure homes with less labor.

Even if none of these is exactly the vacation house you want to build, a study of the floor plans and the way they utilize available space may give you ideas you'll want to incorporate in your own. Fuller details, and in most cases building plans, of the houses shown are available from the organizations to which they are credited. The addresses to which you send inquiries are listed at the back of this book.

OCTAGONAL EXPANSION HOME

This design begins with a 556-square-foot starter unit in which convertible furniture can provide sleeping accommodations in a living room slightly larger than 16′ by 18′. Large wood windows and exposed wood rafters rising to the central peak create an effect of spaciousness. The expansive wood deck, reached through the sliding doors, further contributes to the feeling of extended living area. As shown in the completed floor plan of 1,284 square feet, as many as three bedrooms may be added in any combination, plus a roofed deck if desired. An optional third bath can also be added between bedrooms 1 and 2. If you build in stages, one bathroom can remain unfinished during the initial construction to serve as a closet.

If the starter unit is to be used mainly for weekends and vacations, it may be heated by a fireplace, preferably of the circulating type, or much more effectively by a wood stove. The fireplace or woodstove may later be used as adjuncts to the central heating when the home is expanded and winterized for year-around use. Although the chimney shown is a conventional masonry one, a metal fireplace and chimney could be used to save construction time. Check the local code to be sure that you buy a fireplace-chimney combination approved in your area.

A sliding safety glass or acrylic door opens onto the deck from the living room and also from bedroom No. 3 in the completed house. Corner windows are used in the bedrooms. Note that when bedroom No. 3 is added, the original deck used with the starter unit need not be changed, as its squared end abuts the bedroom wall in which the sliding door is installed. As the deck is of wood, it can easily be expanded later if more outdoor living space is required.

With three bedrooms added to the starter unit, plus an expanded and roofed wood deck, the house becomes an ample year-round home. Additional deck areas can be added, accessible from the bedrooms by sliding doors, if desired, depending on the site.

This is Western Wood Products Association (WWPA) Design No. 14, plans for which are available. For prices of plans and other information, write Home Building Plan Service at the address listed at the end of this book.

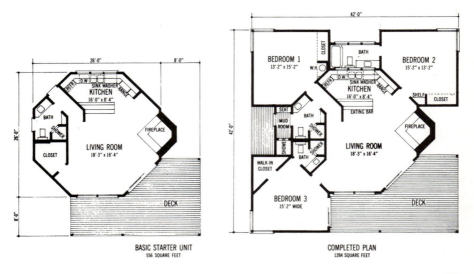

BASIC STARTER UNIT
556 SQUARE FEET

COMPLETED PLAN
1284 SQUARE FEET

CLUSTER SHED

Cluster Sheds are packaged with each piece precisely precut and identified on the piece itself and on the plans and instructions. Sizes of units range from 12′ by 16′ to 16′ by 32′, so designed as to permit joining to form larger structures with a floor plan to suit your needs. Thus, you can start with a small cabin and expand to a large house as your budget permits. You can buy a package containing the frame only, or a "utility package" containing frame, sufficient uncut board-and-batten siding, plus sufficient cedar shake roofing. Or you can buy the complete kit which contains everything from frame to roof, siding, insulation, and inside walls. All you need to provide is the foundation. The 6″ by 6″ timber frame comes with mortises and tenons already cut, ready for locking with oak pegs made for the purpose, as in rugged barns still standing after a century or more. Styrofoam insulation, not shown in the drawing on the opposite page, is used in walls. Small unit is shown at the top of this page, large house of joined units at bottom.

Construction kits and plans are available from Cluster Shed Inc., address at the end of book.

Above, sun deck of large two-level house built by combining Cluster Sheds. Connector sections are built on the site from locally available materials to provide maximum design flexibility. Siding and cedar shakes can be purchased from Cluster Shed manufacturer so connectors will match units. Below, pull-apart drawing shows components of a small Cluster Shed unit. Styrofoam in-wall insulation is not shown, but is part of complete kit.

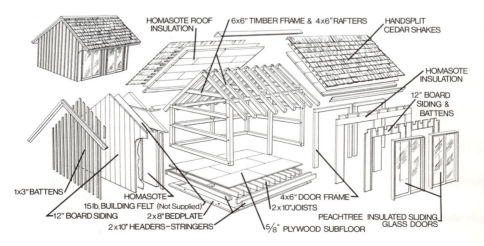

HOMASOTE ROOF INSULATION

6x6" TIMBER FRAME & 4x6" RAFTERS

HANDSPLIT CEDAR SHAKES

HOMASOTE INSULATION

12" BOARD SIDING & BATTENS

1x3" BATTENS

HOMASOTE

15 lb. BUILDING FELT (Not Supplied)

12" BOARD SIDING

2x8" BEDPLATE

2x10" HEADERS—STRINGERS

4x6" DOOR FRAME

2x10" JOISTS

5⁄8" PLYWOOD SUBFLOOR

PEACHTREE INSULATED SLIDING GLASS DOORS

TWO-STORY POLE CABIN

If you'd like an ample summer retreat quickly and economically, this two-story pole cabin may be the answer. As it is supported by poles treated to resist rot and insect attack, the extra time required for construction of a masonry foundation is eliminated. The plan is also available, however, for use with a continous perimeter foundation of masonry. This, of course, can provide a considerable amount of extra living or storage area under the first floor, in which an automatic heating unit could be installed.

The model illustrated above, with its floor plan on the opposite page, is heated by a prefabricated fireplace with factory-built chimney extending up through the second floor bedroom. A woodburing stove can be substituted for the fireplace for added efficiency and the more precise control required to hold a wood fire for extended periods. The open design living room is approximately 21′ 2″ square. The dining area is cantilevered from one side, with bath and utility room extending from the other. A 15′ 2″ by 5′ 7″ kitchen, containing space for refrigerator, sink, dishwasher, and range, opens onto the rear of the living room, partially screened off from it by stairs to the second-floor bedroom.

If a wood-burning stove with a cooktop is used in place of the fireplace, it can serve as a supplementary cooking facility, cutting overall running expenses through double utilization of the firewood. (In cold areas local hardware dealers usually stock wood stoves.) The chimney from the wood stove will radiate a considerable amount of heat into the upstairs bedroom through which it passes. Be sure, however, to use an approved type of chimney, and *only* accessories made by the manufacturer for use with it. This is very important, especially at points where the chimney passes through ceiling and roof, in order to protect the wood structure of the house from excessive temperatures.

If you later winterize your pole cabin (without basement), an automatic central heating unit can be installed in the utility room, with ducts or piping leading to the living areas on both floors. An all-fuel chimney may be used with the central heating unit.

A 4'-wide deck, shielded by the front roof overhang, provides outdoor dining space beyond the front wall of the living room. Access to the deck from the living room is provided by sliding glass or acrylic doors. Steps from the deck lead to ground level.

Cabin is Western Wood Products Plan No. 21, available from Home Building Plan Service.

SECOND FLOOR PLAN
256 SQUARE FEET

Upstairs bedroom is 12' 2" by 15' 3". Stairs start parallel to the rear of the house on the first floor, turn to run parallel to the main roof gable ends on the second floor for the best headroom under the sloping ceiling of the bedroom. Fireplace or heating stove on the first floor is located so the chimney will not encroach on the bedroom window areas. Follow manufacturer's instructions for protection of exposed chimney sections.

MAIN FLOOR PLAN
640 SQUARE FEET

Main floor area of 640 square feet may be laid out as shown at left, or varied to suit your individual requirements. If cabin is pole-supported and is to be used in winter, provision must be made to protect water supply and drainage pipes in the space between the floor and the ground frost line. This can be done by insulated enclosure and electric heating cables made for use on pipes. Cables are available from building supply dealers and electrical supply houses.

THE OMEGADOME

The geodesic dome can be erected and weatherproofed in as little as three days. The design shown, is available from American Geodesic, Inc. Vertical walls on three sides provide space for windows and doors or standard design, with storage space and low headroom areas (counters and built-ins) situated in the low-roofed portions. Each unit yields up to 1,000 square feet of floor area, made up of 800 square feet of basic floor space plus 200 square feet of loft. This is the equivalent of a 25' by 40' rectangular area. The units can be combined in a variety of ways to form a still larger structure. Each form is available in a type adapted to a full foundation and wood deck, a wood deck and platform on posts or pads, or a concrete slab foundation.

Several construction arrangements are offered for the Omegadome. Number 1 is based on a frame kit that includes the struts that comprise the framework. This kit provides the predrilled parts that make up the individual triangles for the framing, color-coded for easy assembly, and including the steel brackets used in the construction. You provide your own plywood from local sources, for covering the frames. The Number 2 kit, termed the Panel Kit, provides the triangular panels already covered with plywood, predrilled and ready to bolt together. You obtain your roofing material locally.

If you want your Omegadome assembled (rather than doing it yourself), the manufacturer can supply a crew or a technician to serve as a consultant and guide to a local construction crew. Depending on your building ability, choose your arrangement after contacting the manufacturer.

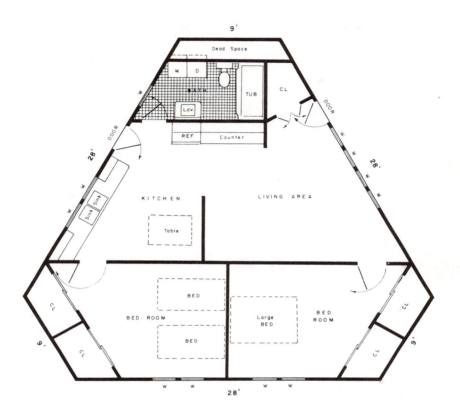

Interior view of Omegadome inside the front door is shown at right. Vertical walls permit use of conventional doors, while geodesic design results in exotic ceiling form and structural economies. One of a variety of floor plans for Omegadome, suited to single family as a vacation home, is shown above. The manufacturer can provide plans for many other layouts to suit individual requirements. To obtain the plan best matched to your needs, check the basic plans and decide which one best suits your situation. Modifications can be made as needed.

A-FRAME VACATION HOME

Simplicity of construction is the keynote of this A-frame vacation home. Twenty-eight feet from front to back, with decks adjoining front and rear, the house provides ample indoor and outdoor living space. A centrally located prefab fireplace with metal chimney provides the heat. (A thermostatically controlled wood-burning heater could be substituted for convenience if the house is to be used for prolonged periods in winter.)

The first-floor plan includes a 24′ 11″ by 11′ 6″ living room plus bedroom, bath, kitchen, and ample storage space. The total inside living area is 952 square feet. A loft above the rear portion of the house (with railed balcony at front) can be furnished as a second bedroom. Exposed beams and warm-toned wood paneling accent the interior.

Oriented with its picture-windowed front facing south, the house can be partially heated by the sun. The generous roof overhang can be planned to shade the window area in summer when the sun is higher in the sky.

Plans for this design (No. 15) are available from Home Building Plan Service.

First-floor layout of A-frame. As the side walls slope, the lower portion is used for storage, with closet doors in vertical kneewalls. Counters in the kitchen and furnishings in other rooms of the A-frame are arranged to utilize low headroom space along the side walls. The slope of the stairway matches that of the roof, to provide headroom where needed at the top of the stairs.

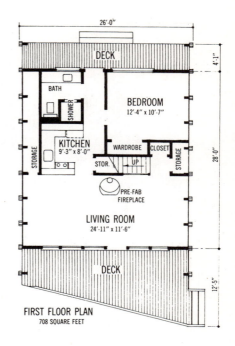

26'-0"

DECK

4'-1"

BATH

SHOWER

BEDROOM
12'-4" x 10'-7"

28'-0"

STORAGE

KITCHEN
9'-3" x 8'-0"

WARDROBE CLOSET

STOR. UP

STORAGE

PRE-FAB
FIREPLACE

LIVING ROOM
24'-11" x 11'-6"

DECK

12'-5"

FIRST FLOOR PLAN
708 SQUARE FEET

Forward section of house, containing living room, has high, peaked ceiling with exposed rafters. The loft in the rear section is above kitchen, bath, and bedroom, with stairs leading up to a railed balcony. Drapes over front and back windows provide privacy.

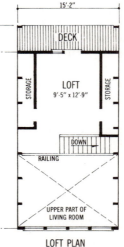

15'-2"

DECK

STORAGE

LOFT
9'-5" x 12'-9"

STORAGE

DOWN

RAILING

UPPER PART OF
LIVING ROOM

LOFT PLAN
244 SQUARE FEET

33

EXPANSION HOME

Shown above as a pole cabin, this design can start as a small unit with a mere 320 square feet of floor area, as at left, and expand to a two-bedroom house with 992 square feet. The initial unit can be used as an operational headquarters while expanding the building. Note that extra rooms may be added to the right of the original unit, as in the second stage or to the left. The final stage (lower right) includes additions on the left and right of the original unit. If you plan to build the complete unit, a perimeter foundation may be used to provide a basement to increase the total living area and to provide space for a central heating system. A deck and slanted railing are features of all of the units, providing outdoor living space.

The large window areas should be oriented with regard to the time of day the different rooms will be used, and also to utilize solar heating insofar as possible. An eastern exposure in bedrooms provides morning sunlight, a western exposure in the living room offers warming sunlight during the afternoon hours when guests are likely, and a southern exposure of any large window area contributes to heating economy throughout the daylight hours.

Although shown on pole supports, the various versions of this design might also be built on masonry piers or, as mentioned, on a perimeter foundation. A partial cellar can cut excavation costs while still providing full headroom for a central heating unit, if the house is to be winterized. If the heating unit is located at one end, a factory-built chimney may be installed outside the house wall.

Plans are available from the Home Building Plan Service. The numbers are: small unit, 24A; second stage, 24B; alternate second stage, 24C; final stage, 24D, and final stage with perimeter foundation, 24E.

FIRST STAGE
PLAN WWP-24A
320 SQUARE FEET

SECOND STAGE
PLAN WWP-24B
608 SQUARE FEET

Floor plans of the four versions of expandable vacation house. You can start with the small unit at upper left, and increase the size as budget permits, or begin with one of the larger units. If the house is to be winterized, plan on heating system from the start and install full insulation during construction. If the house is on poles or piers, insulate the floor.

ALTERNATE SECOND STAGE
PLAN WWP-24C
704 SQUARE FEET

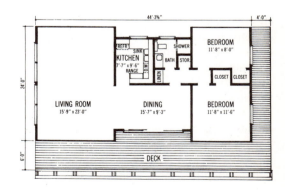

PLAN WWP-24D FINAL STAGE POLE FOUNDATION
PLAN WWP-24E FINAL STAGE PERIMETER FOUNDATION
992 SQUARE FEET

OCTAGONAL SECOND HOME

If your second home is planned to be your permanent home in time to come, this exotic octagonal design offers features that place it in a distinctive category of its own. The unique design with oriental overtones provides almost every part of the house with an exterior wall and a window view. The first-floor living area is designed in the style of an open studio, wrapping around a major portion of the house and featuring a massive fireplace, open on two sides. A separate kitchen, laundry, and lavatory complete the layout for convenience and privacy. Three decks extend the living area outdoors.

A balcony hallway connects all second-floor bedrooms and provides access to the bath. A centrallly located skylight admits sunlight to both floors through an open center area of the second floor. Abundant storage space is provided on both levels, which are connected by an open staircase. Floors throughout are of wood, with exposed wood structural supports and wood paneling. Exterior siding is 1-by-6 tongue-and-groove boards. The roof is hand-split shakes. If four bedrooms are not required, one may be replaced with a deck, as shown in the alternate second-floor plan. Sheltered by the roof, such an upper deck provides an ideal area for warm-weather entertaining, with an expansive view and protection from the summer sun.

Spacious enough for a large family or frequent overnight guests, this house is easily adaptable to any conventional system of central heating. Site planning, of course, should include consideration of orientation to provide sun and shade at times best suited to your life style, and to take advantage of the most desirable view from living areas and decks.

The plan is No. 27, available from Home Building Plan Service.

If less than the four bedrooms are required, one may be eliminated to provide an upper-level deck, as shown at right. Access to the deck, provided by sliding glass doors, also provides additional light to the upper balcony hallway. The deck may be glassed in if winter use is likely.

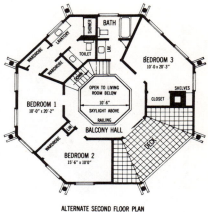

ALTERNATE SECOND FLOOR PLAN
1170 SQUARE FEET
(1260 SQUARE FEET—INCLUDING DECK)

For a large family or frequent overnight guests, the upper level may include four bedrooms. The master bedroom (No. 1) has its own private bath. The second bath serves the other bedrooms, as does the lavatory on the first floor. All bedrooms have windows on two facets of the octagon.

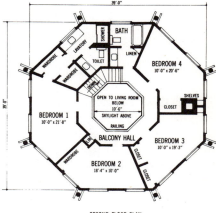

SECOND FLOOR PLAN
1260 SQUARE FEET

Large party deck adjacent to living and dining area of the first floor is on the opposite side of the house from the entrance deck. Service deck is accessible from kitchen through the back door next to the laundry. Smaller decks and inner portion of party deck are sheltered by the overhang of second floor (dotted lines).

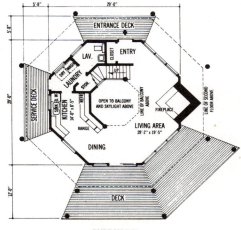

FIRST FLOOR PLAN
697 SQUARE FEET

RANCH FOR ALL SEASONS

With three bedrooms and two baths, this one-story design can serve as a vacation home or as a year-around home for the entire family. Dimensions of the house exclusive of deck and overhangs are 46′ by 24′, for a total inside living area of 1,104 square feet. With all rooms on the same level, the design provides convenience and ample storage space. If additional room is required, the house can be built with a full basement. Where the terrain permits a walkout basement, it can include more sleeping accommodations. Otherwise it can be finished as a family room, workshop, and utility room for a central heating unit. If built on a slab without a basement, the space made available by elimination of the basement stairs, with slight modification, can be used to house a compact central heating unit.

The wrap-around wood deck (accessible through sliding glass doors from the living room) not only provides ample space for outdoor entertaining, but afford an easy route to the carport. Vertical wood siding is used on both the house and the enclosed portion of the carport. Exposed roof framing members add to the natural effect of the outside living area's decor. Finish is a matter of individual preference, though a woodsy brown on railings and deck surfaces, with a lighter tone on the siding, creates an attractive combination that requires little maintenance.

As the house may be built with or without a basement, it adapts readily to most building sites. If built without a basement in an outlying area where the water supply is provided by a drilled deep well on the property, a submersible pump may be used in the well. This eliminates all sound of pump operation inside the house, and requires space only for the water storage tank,

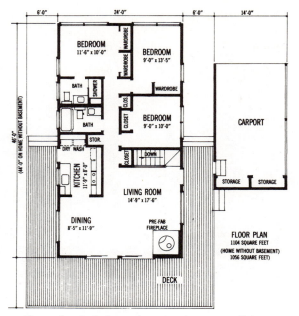

| 6'-0" | 24'-0" | 6'-0" | 14'-0" |

BEDROOM
11'-6" x 10'-0"

WARDROBE

BEDROOM
9'-0" x 13'-5"

WARDROBE

BATH

SHOWER

CLOS.

CARPORT

CLOSET

BEDROOM
9'-0" x 10'-0"

BATH

STOR.

DRY WASH

46'-0"
(44'-0" ON HOME WITHOUT BASEMENT)

CLOSET

DOWN

KITCHEN
11'-9" x 8'-0"

STORAGE   STORAGE

LIVING ROOM
14'-9" x 17'-6"

DINING
8'-5" x 11'-9"

PRE-FAB
FIREPLACE

FLOOR PLAN
1104 SQUARE FEET
(HOME WITHOUT BASEMENT)
1056 SQUARE FEET)

DECK

Floor plan includes stairway to basement. If house is built without basement, stairway space may be used for other purposes. Storage space at walled end of carport is shown without doors, but doors may be used to protect contents from weather and to allow for locks.

which can be installed in a small portion of the storage space, as in part of a closet. It is essential, however, that a water-storage tank be well insulated to prevent condensation on its surface and resultant dampness. In the walkout basement version illustrated, a portion of the space under the main deck area is used for storing firewood for a prefab fireplace. An all-fuel metal chimney can be used with the fireplace, and an additional one for the central heating unit, if the house is winterized.

The carport provides storage space for garden tools and other necessities at the walled end. Like many carports, it can be completely enclosed and fitted with a roll-up door if desired.

Plans for the house are available from Home Building Plan Service. For the house with basement, the plan number No. 18; without basement, the plan is No. 18A.

LOG BUILDINGS, FROM CABINS TO MANSIONS

Precut log buildings are available in sizes and styles that range from the traditional form shown above, to the lavish two-bedroom home shown on page **43**. Both have solid cedar walls and are made by the same company, Boyne Falls Log Homes. The homes produced by this and other firms are improved versions of the early American log cabin. For example, the seams between logs are sealed with a spline as well as with caulking or gasket material, to make a windproof wall. Tests on scale models have shown such walls to have an insulating quality actually superior to conventional stud walls. A variation of the log design features the use of vertical, rather than horizontal logs, or a combination of the two styles. Whatever type you choose is shipped precut to your building site. You can do the construction work yourself, guided by the manufacturer's instructions, or have it done by professionals. Some log building manufacturers will provide a crew or an experienced supervisor for a price, or arrange construction through a dealer in your area. Some will also design a precut house according to your own floor plan if the available designs don't match your requirements. These are among the points you may want to cover when you plan to build a precut log house. Of course, it's wise to check the building and zoning departments (if there are codes) in the area where you plan to build. You'll find the addresses of several manufacturers of precut log building at the end of this book.

Interior of a typical solid wall log house. Inside surface of logs is flat and smooth, requiring no paint or wallpaper. Structural timbers are exposed as part of the decor. Outside of wall logs are left naturally round, but with bark removed. Cedar weathers to a silver gray. This cabin is from Boyne Falls Log Homes.

AS TRADITIONAL AS YOU LIKE IT

If you want the interior of your log house to resemble that of log houses built a century ago or earlier, you can have a precut version with log surfaces naturally round on the inside as well as the outside, like this one by Vermont Log Buildings, Inc. Three complete sets of working drawings and a 32-page construction guide are supplied with each home. Doors and windows are pre-hung in their frames for easy installation. When wiring is installed it can be concealed inside the first log, which is designed for that purpose. Plumbing can be concealed in conventionally framed interior partition walls. Homes by this firm are available in many sizes and styles.

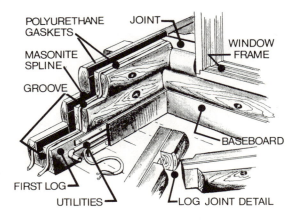

Cutaway drawing of solid log wall. Splines and gaskets seal seams between logs to make wall windproof. Same combination seals joints wherever end-to-end joints are required. Wiring and water-supply lines can be concealed in first log, behind baseboard. Logs are joined at corners as shown.

CHOOSE YOUR STYLE AND SIZE

This cabin, one of Ward Cabin Company's series of Allagash designs in the lower price range, is built with northern white cedar logs, used horizontally and vertically. This is a species with very high insulating qualities. For a wind seal between the logs, a tongue-and-groove system is used in place of splines. The logs are milled flat on the top, bottom, and inside surfaces and have a groove in the bottom surface, a tongue projecting from the top surface. The interior surface is planed smooth to present a warm paneled effect when finished. If you want smooth painted or papered walls in any of the rooms, wallboard may be applied over the log surface. In extremely cold climates, a layer of foam insulation may be mounted between the wallboard and the log surface, adding to the insulating effect of the solid log construction. No special tools are necessary for the construction work. Where wall logs join end to end they are milled at the factory with half-lapped ends to assure windproof joints. Chimney location depends on heating arrangements. This one uses a fieldstone chimney outside the wall, built through the roof overhang, thus simplifying the installation of flashing where masonry materials are not economical, or building time is limited, a metal chimney can be used for a fireplace, wood-burning heater, or central heating unit.

BEFORE YOU BUY. Because of the wide variety of styles and sizes of log buildings made by different manufacturers, and because of individual features, be sure you have the information you need before you buy. And ask about special services. You may find that the manufacturer will plan a custom home the way you want it. Look at the brochures you receive as a result of your initial inquiries, and ask for current prices and for suggestions on financing. Be sure to find out about details you will be living with in your completed house. Some precuts, for example, have flat-planed interior log surfaces, while others have rounded log surfaces inside and out. Pick the one you want. Be sure that you know just what is included in the home package you buy, so you can plan for overall costs. Usually, it's the house itself, not including wiring, plumbing, or heating. You'll want recommendations on installation of all three. A precut log home can be a real bargain if you plan carefully.

CHAPTER FOUR

TOOLS FOR BUILDING YOUR VACATION HOME

How WELL you build, how quickly the work goes, and whether it's enjoyable or sheer labor depends in large part on the tools you use. It is a truism worth restating that cheap tools are not really economical. They make you work harder for inferior results.

Buy good brand-named tools whenever possible. Even such an apparently simple one as a hammer can be wrong in some respects. A head of poor quality or temper may chip, or the claws may break when stressed. Poor balance makes a hammer tiring to use, and can be responsible for any number of bent nails. Even the crown and polish of the striking surface are important.

Edged tools are still more critical. You will quickly discern the difference between a good and a poor saw if you have the opportunity to use both. But if you handicap yourself with a poor one and use no other, you may blame yourself for poor work due to its shortcomings.

It is not necessary to buy all the tools you will need at one time. Many amateur builders add to their collection of tools only as the need arises. You are less likely to buy unnecessary ones this way, and can stretch the cash outlay over a reasonable period. Some items that you will need only for a short time, such as concrete mixers and floor sanders, can be rented.

HAND TOOLS. For laying the foundation, you will have to have a plumb line and a good level. Both will be required all through the construction work. Also needed are digging implements (a pick or mattock, and a spade), a hatchet to sharpen and drive stakes, a wheelbarrow for hauling stones, and a hoe for mixing small batches of concrete.

Types of Saws. A good 24″ or 26″ crosscut saw with eight points (teeth) per inch is your number one carpentry tool. For trimming stock to odd widths, get a ripsaw. It will have larger teeth than the crosscut saw, but only five and a half per inch, and differently sharpened. Eventually you will probably need a keyhole saw, and perhaps a coping saw, for finishing the interior and making built-in furniture.

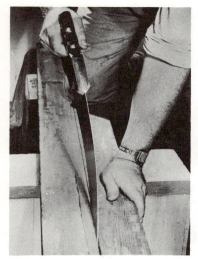

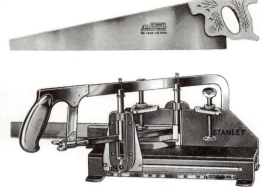

Ripsaw (left) is handy for trimming stock. Crosscut saw (top) is important hand tool on any job. Get one that is taper ground, minimum 24" long. Miter box and back saw (above) are valuable for making precision angle cuts on moldings and door trim.

Your chief hammer should have a 16- or 20-ounce head; a lighter 13-ounce one will be useful for fitting molding and other small jobs. A nail set is necessary to drive finishing nails below the surface, and a screwdriver for various odd chores such as mounting hardware.

The large steel square known as a framing square is vital not only for checking 90-degree corners, but also for setting out angle cuts on rafters and stair stringers.

A plane is useful for smoothing surfaces and trimming edges of doors and windows to fit their openings. It need not be larger than a jack plane (9" or 14" long), but it should be a good one. If you are faced with fitting much trim or molding around corners, a miter box and a backsaw will be worth having. They make it easy to cut precise miter angles.

Hand Drilling Tools. Two tools are needed for making holes by hand—a hand brace for those larger than ¼", and a hand drill for smaller ones. With these you will need auger bits of various sizes, and a set of twist drills in fractional-inch sizes from $\frac{1}{16}$" to ¼".

Two chisels, ½" and 1" wide, are useful for cutting lock mortises and hinge gains.

Once carpentry begins, a couple of stout sawhorses become indispensable.

Fine work on interiors calls for keyhole saw. This one cuts metal, plastic and wood with interchangeable blades.

Use framing square to check right angles, lay out rafters, stairs and joist bridging.

Jack plane aids in smoothing stock, fitting doors and windows in their openings.

You can make them out of 2-by-4s, with lighter lumber for cross bracing. Or you can use ingenious hardware that makes their construction a simple matter of screwing or clamping the wooden members in place.

For hand drilling of holes over ¼", use a brace and auger bit. Ratchet head allows you to work with brace in tight spots.

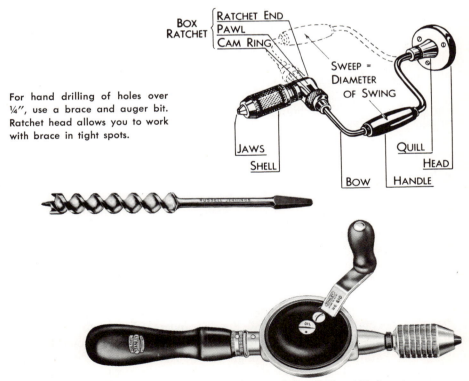

Hand drill bores small holes in wood with twist drills 1/16" to ¼" diameter.

ELECTRIC POWER TOOLS. Where electric power is available at all, it may be possible to get a service connection made before the house is begun. For such temporary service, however, you may have to build a weatherproof enclosure to house the shutoff switch and outlet, if not the meter as well. Check with your power company before you decide to buy electric power tools. If the power line does not run near your property, there may be a surcharge or, indeed, it may prove too costly to get service at all. But if electricity is to be connected to the finished house, it is possible that you can get service in advance by installing the basic equipment required by local codes and the utility company.

If you already have workshop tools and a station wagon or the like to haul them in, your table saw and jointer may prove useful in building a vacation home. So, to a lesser extent, may a bandsaw, drill press and sander. But as there will be no shelter for such tools until the house is partially built, you will probably have to haul them to the site and back every time you use them.

Portable Tools. For this and other reasons, portable power tools are really more suitable. You can haul several of these in the smallest car, with far less effort than is involved in carrying stationary power tools. For house construction, the portable tools are even more useful, since they go right to the work instead of having the work brought to them. Portable tools can often cut, drill or smooth pieces already nailed in place.

Electric tools are rated by the Underwriters' Laboratories for either home or industrial use. An industrial rating means the tool meets higher standards of electrical safety and heat dissipation, among other things. Manufacturers further grade their different tools with respect to the service that may reasonably be expected from them. One large maker, for example, lists "utility," "deluxe" and "professional" tools. The lowest-priced utility line, though eminently suited for odd-job home use, is not designed to stand up under hard all-day service. The medium-priced deluxe tools are for heavier duty, have more power and should be worth their modest cost difference to the leisure-home builder. The top-quality professional line, meant for the full-time carpenter or contractor, is designed for maximum efficiency under continuous service.

Any electric tool you buy should carry the Underwriters' Laboratories insignia. Unless it is one of the comparatively few having an all-plastic casing and handle, it should be fitted with a three-prong plug that grounds it for your safety, as explained farther on.

Circular Saw. In trained hands, a portable circular saw can do the work of three experts armed with hand saws. It zips through such standard stock as 2-by-6s in seconds. Used with a protractor, rip fence or other guide, it can crosscut, miter-cut or rip accurately. It can also make notches and dadoes, slice big plywood sheets to size, saw flooring and roof boards to length after they're in place, form edge and end dadoes. For the vacation-home builder, it is probably the most important single tool he can have.

A good 6½" saw is able to cut through the 2" dimension of a dressed 2-by-4 at 45 degrees. This is adequate for most of the jobs you will be doing. How-

Portable electric circular saw is workhorse on job. It should have at least a 6½" blade. *Courtesy Black & Decker Co.*

ever, a larger (7¼" or 7½") saw not only cuts slightly deeper but being more powerful is also a bit speedier. Professional 8" saws are even more capable, but they are also heavier and not as easy for the amateur to handle.

See that the saw you buy has a sturdy blade guard above, and a freely working retractable lower guard that returns automatically—and reliably— after the blade is through the cut. It should also have a sturdy rip fence and clearly marked, properly calibrated tilt and depth gauges, with convenient lock nuts. A safety clutch is desirable.

Electric Drill. This versatile tool will not only make holes but do many other tasks, from mixing paint to driving screws. You can even buy attachments to convert it to a circular saw, a sabre saw, a plane, or a sander. However, such accessories are for light duty only. They are less capable and less convenient than individual tools. For construction work, they can hardly be considered adequate substitutes.

As a hole maker and for a few other odd chores, however, a ⅜" electric drill is very useful. This size is both capable and light enough for easy handling.

A drill's size designation means it can make holes of that size in steel. With suitable bits, it can make much larger holes in wood, wallboard and other softer materials. High-speed twist drills are the kind to buy for making holes in metal; they cost more but stand up much better than the cheaper carbon drills, which are not truly suitable for use under power. For making holes in wood, you can buy special auger bits (don't use the kind meant for a hand brace) or spade bits. The latter are cheaper but adequate. They come in sizes from ¼" to 1¼". Larger holes can be made with either a fly cutter or, more satisfactorily, with a hole saw. The former is adjustable to a wide range of sizes, whereas hole saws come in stepped sizes to 3".

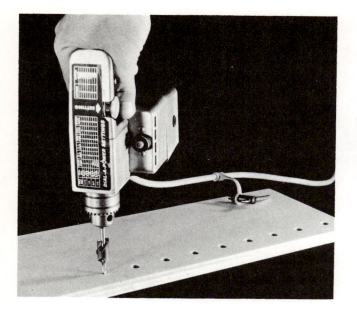

This power drill allows you to switch speeds according to material being drilled. *Courtesy Disston Co.*

An important electric-tool development is an electronic circuit that senses the work load and feeds more current to the motor as required, holding speed constant even if the work becomes harder. With one ⅜″ drill so equipped you can shift speeds between 600 and 2,000 revolutions per minute to suit the job, the high speed for small holes in metal, a medium speed for larger holes, or low speed for such rugged jobs as swinging a 3″ hole saw. Other tools with this feature are sure to come along.

Sabre Saw. Sometimes called a jigsaw, this tool has a short, stiff, narrow blade held at one end only. It can be guided along curved cuts as well as straight ones. One sabre saw, with the electronic speed control described above, can be run slowly for cutting steel or plastic, at intermediate speed for other metals, or at high speed for cutting wood.

A surprising feature is the sabre saw's ability to make internal cuts without starting from a hole. This is done by tilting the tool so that only the front of its shoe rests on the work surface, and then gradually lowering the reciprocating blade until it cuts through. It's a handy technique for cutting openings for wall niches, cabinets or electric-outlet boxes in walls.

A good sabre saw will also rip, crosscut, and notch stock. With a guide bar swinging on a nail, it can cut perfect circles of almost any size. However, it won't do straight cutting at the speed of a circular saw, especially in thick-

Spade bits for portable power drill bore holes in wood from ⅜″ to 1″ diameter.

Sabre saw excels in curves, mid-panel cuts, but it also rips and crosscuts. *Stanley Tools.*

nesses above ¼". You may wish to defer buying a sabre saw until you begin finishing the interior of your vacation home, when it will be useful for various fitting jobs, cutting curved edges and corners, and making round table tops.

There is a heavy-duty sabre saw, however, which is in a class by itself and may be of interest to log-cabin builders. Its long blade can cut through small logs or notch these for half-lap corner joints or window frames.

Sanders. One of the most time-consuming jobs the builder faces is sanding. If you plan to sand floors, it will pay to rent a floor sander rather than buy one. For many lesser jobs, a rubber-backed sanding disk used in your electric drill will serve.

But if there is much trim to be sanded, or built-in or unfinished furniture to be smoothed preparatory to finishing, a separate sander is worth having. The orbital sander (so-called because it moves the platen or shoe carrying the abrasive in a tight little circle) is a popular and efficient type. This kind is especially effective in smoothing plywood edges, for the orbital action sands down all the plies equally.

The straight-line sander moves the platen back and forth in one direction. Its chief advantage is that all sanding can be done with the grain, which is desirable for maximum smoothness. Cross-grain sanding removes stock faster, so where you want to sand out scratches you can hold the machine with its straight-line action across or at an angle to the wood grain.

Straight-line sanders generally have a vibratory motor instead of a rotary one, and therefore no motor brushes, bearings or shafts to wear. As a minor disadvantage, they tend to cut down some of the plies in plywood edges more than others; the end-grain plies are left a trifle higher. One rotary-motor sander has dual action, switching from orbital to straight-line action at the flip of a lever.

Orbital sander is good all-round finishing tool. It works well on plywood edges.

Straight-line sander moves back and forth only for with-the-grain finishing.

For heavy-duty sanding, there are portable belt sanders. The abrasive is in the form of a wide belt that travels over rollers, one of which is motor driven. A powerful belt sander makes quick work of removing stock. It's so much faster than a plane, it must be carefully handled to avoid spoiling the work. It can be used for fitting doors and window sash, smoothing big counters, furniture surfaces and wallboard joints.

GAS-POWERED TOOLS. You needn't do without power tools even if there is no utility line to connect them to. One solution is a portable 115-volt alternating-current generator of your own. A gasoline-powered rig of 2,500-

For tough sanding jobs, belt sander is best bet. It'll do the work of a plane.

watts capacity will run just about any portable power tool, including a 7¼″ circular saw, provided you exercise some care not to overload the tool. But don't expect such a plant to run two or more tools at once, or a string of lights besides. The cost of a generating plant is considerable, and a factor in your decision to buy one will be whether it can provide lighting current for your leisure home afterwards.

Several manufacturers offer a different solution in the form of tools with their own gasoline engines. These are strictly for outdoor use. They cannot be put to work in an even partially enclosed structure for their exhaust is fully as deadly as an automobile's.

The first gas-powered tool to become popular was perhaps the chain saw, which has an endless motor-driven chain carrying saw teeth around a rigid plate. A diaphragm-type carburetor enables the motor to run no matter how you tilt it.

Gas-powered chain saw speeds log-cabin building. It is strictly for outdoor use.

The development of a phenomenal pint-sized gas engine by a famous maker of model-airplane engines has given rise to several new self-powered tools. One is a 9-pound chain saw. Despite its small size, it's claimed this saw can cut through a 6″ log in fifteen seconds. List price is $118. You can, of course, get larger chain saws that have even greater work capacity.

The small engine mentioned has also been put to work in three ½″ drills, priced from $90 up. Although they tote their own engine, all are of surprisingly modest weight; one tips the scales at 8 pounds, another at 10½. Their high cost, however, puts rather a premium on the convenience of boring holes by power instead of with a hand drill or brace.

There is little question, on the other hand, that an 8″ portable circular saw driven by the same minute engine can be as good as an extra helper in building your vacation home. This peppy little saw cuts up to 2⅜″ deep at 90 degrees, whisks through 2-by-8s in four or five seconds, slices ¾″ plywood at the rate of 10 feet per minute. That's considerably faster than the ordinary 6½″ electric saw; the tool has plenty of power. It lists for about $120.

Two rugged gas-powered saws: circular saw (above) and reciprocating saw (left).

BATTERY-POWERED TOOLS. Black & Decker's cordless drill, the first to be run by self-contained, rechargeable batteries, drills small holes about as rapidly as ordinary cord-powered ¼″ drills. It will even make holes in masonry, given suitable bits. But it slows down on the job as hole size goes up, and under continuous use its charge is exhausted in about an hour. It's only fair to point out, though, that like any battery source it recovers somewhat if allowed occasional rest periods. Also, in one nonstop test, it bored 174 holes of ¼″ diameter in ¾″ pine on a single charge.

Recharging takes at least five hours, which makes overnight the logical time for this chore. The tool is quieter than ordinary drills and weighs only 4 pounds, batteries and all. But you do pay extra for that self-powered feature. You must buy a charger for the batteries.

The Skil Corporation offers a self-powered drill, a sabre saw and a sander (in addition to grass shears and a hedge trimmer). All these tools have cords, but they plug into a portable battery pack you hang at your belt. Being larger than any that could be built into the tools, the power package is more potent. Tool capacity is good and a charge will do more work.

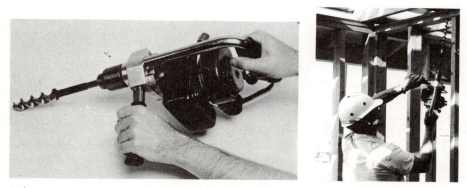

Light, compact gas-powered drill tackles tough drilling chores on building job. *Courtesy Comet Industries Corp.*

Battery-powered drill bores small holes fast, but it needs overnight recharging after heavy use.

More battery-powered tools will surely appear. As yet they are modestly powered and of course must be recharged frequently. Gas-powered tools, on the other hand, have more than ample power and can be operated indefinitely far from electric lines.

THE SHOCK HAZARD. Battery- and gas-powered tools are of course shock-free, except for the annoyance of touching a spark plug, which isn't dangerous even though unpleasant. From this standpoint they are much safer than plug-in electric tools for outdoor work.

There is a very real (and possibly lethal) risk in the careless use of 115-volt tools outdoors, especially during wet weather or on damp ground. Because one conductor of any electric utility line is grounded, even a slight defect that doesn't impair the tool's operation can create a dangerous shock hazard. It is to eliminate this that good portable power tools come with three-wire cords and three-prong plugs.

Many users circumvent the safety these are meant to provide by using an adapter to connect such plugs to ordinary two-hole outlets, but ignoring the little pigtail of wire on the adapter. If this is left hanging free, the user is quite unprotected from the effects of an internal short in the tool.

The pigtail is meant to be securely fastened under the screw that holds on the outlet plate, or to be connected to some other well-grounded metal fixture, such as a water pipe.

It is better still to plug the tool into a three-hole outlet designed for the purpose. Properly installed, such outlets automatically ground the tool. If you install equipment for temporary service, make sure that the outlet provided is of this type, and that it is correctly grounded. It's a precaution you owe yourself and any helpers you may have.

HOW EXTENSIONS CAN TRIP YOU. Should you use an extension cord between the outlet and a power-tool cord, the extension also must be of the three-wire type, with a three-prong plug at one end and a three-hole socket at the other. Using a two-wire extension nullifies all shock protection because the grounding does not extend to the tool.

Another pitfall in the use of extensions is excessive voltage drop. Just any extension long enough to stretch the required distance will not do. Unless its conductors are of a certain minimum gauge, the voltage at the far end will be too low to operate the tool efficiently. It will stall prematurely under load at best; at worst, the substandard voltage can make the motor draw excessive current and burn out.

Manufacturers specify the size of extension conductors required to operate each tool at a certain distance from the outlet. Check with your tool dealer to be sure of having full power and to avoid costly motor damage. Make sure your extension has conductors heavy enough to accommodate your heaviest tool (usually the circular saw). It will then safely operate any lighter tool.

THE DIFFERENCE AN EDGE MAKES. Should your saw or drill seem to have less power than it previously did, take a sharp look at the blade or bits it is turning. Dull ones take a lot of extra power, which does no useful work. A dull saw tends to burn the cut surface, requires more effort, and may tend to wander off the line. Check the set (alternate side offset) of saw teeth; it may have suffered from hitting an exceptionally hard knot or a nail. Dull drills readily overheat and may refuse to work in metal at all. Dull wood bits burn the wood and require excessive feed pressure. Both overload the drill motor. In the case of battery-powered tools, they severely reduce the amount of work obtainable from a charge.

CHAPTER FIVE

LOCATING AND BUILDING THE FOUNDATION

HAVING BOUGHT a site and selected a house plan, you must decide exactly where the structure is to stand and how it is to be oriented—for example, whether it will face the entrance road or a lovely lake. But this is not merely a matter of aesthetic choice. Also involved are summer and winter comfort, possible later additions, freedom from water damage, and safety.

It may be tempting to build against a hillside that will shelter the house from northerly storms and winds. But the hill may also cut off cooling breezes in hot weather. More important, there is a possibility of damage from surface water. If you build on a slope, make sure the house won't be in the path of heavy rain runoff, which sometimes creates streams where none existed before. Evidence of these often remains in the form of gullies and similar results of soil erosion.

Any house with much of a slope above it should be protected from surface runoff by a diversionary barrier that will detour water around it (Fig. 1). This may be a ditch (which will have to be kept clear of choking weeds and dirt), a masonry wall or, though less satisfactory, soil banked up against the foundation.

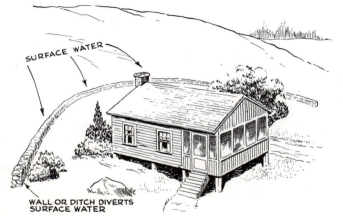

SURFACE WATER

WALL OR DITCH DIVERTS
SURFACE WATER

Fig. 1. Stone wall acts as a barrier against surface runoff.

Should you build on a hillside shelf, be sure to grade it so that there is a drainage slope away from the house. Otherwise the building site becomes a basin to accumulate water under the house.

It is generally unwise to locate a house under overhanging rocks or big earth banks which may some time be undermined by rains. In snow country, beware of slopes likely to become chutes for snow slides or avalanches, especially those at the bottom of a "V" formed by surrounding terrain.

If your land is on a lake or stream, take the trouble to find out how high flood waters have risen. Locating the house a few feet higher can make all the difference between flood damage and security some rainy spring.

THE WEATHER ANGLE. What weather exposure is best depends largely on when the leisure home will be occupied. If it's for winter fun, you will get more warmth from what sunshine there is by locating on a southern or southeastern slope. This will also afford some shelter from chill north winds. The biggest windows should be on the south side of the house, with heavy drapes or shutters on them to reduce heat loss when the sun is hidden.

But most vacation homes are for summer occupancy, when the problem is too much heat. Breezes may be cut off from a depression or valley, but blow freely a few yards higher up. Visiting your site during hot weather may yield valuable clues about this and help you locate your house favorably.

Sun heat is most oppressive during the afternoon, so shade on the west side of a summer home is desirable. The sun's rays can be screened more effectively during the middle of the day, when the sun is high, than in the morning or late afternoon. For this reason the house should be turned with its larger walls facing north and south, its smaller end walls east and west. Glass admits more heat than walls, so for summer comfort picture windows should be on the north side.

If for any reason you want glass exposure on the south, there are other ways to control sun heat. One is a wide roof overhang. Since the sun stands higher in summer than in winter, a properly designed overhang will cast a shadow on the south side of the structure during most of the day (Fig. 2). In winter, when the sun's path across the sky is at a lower angle, the overhang will allow welcome warmth to enter during much of the day. High trees on the south afford good natural shade, and if they are the kind that shed their leaves, the bare branches will admit sunlight during the colder months.

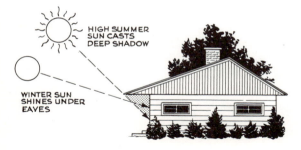

Fig. 2. Wide roof overhang on south side of house provides shade in summer, warmth from lower winter sun.

Light-colored exterior walls and roofs reflect more of the sun's heat than do dark ones. Venetian blinds (which should also be light in color) are almost twice as effective in rejecting heat when mounted outside a window than when they are inside. If a roof overhang is not desirable or practical, window overhangs may be advisable. To keep the early morning and late afternoon sun off the south wall, such overhangs should be enclosed at both ends as shown, or long enough to screen the window even when the sun is low.

Another useful shield against sun heat is the kind of window screening shaped like miniature louvers instead of mesh. Properly installed (outside the glass, of course, and with the louvers angled downwards) this greatly reduces heat transmission through south-oriented windows. It is much less effective, however, in east and west windows because of the lower sun angle there.

For east and west walls, comparatively small trees and even lattice fences are quite effective. Awnings too may help.

You will enjoy a cooler porch or terrace if it is on the north side. There is another reason to put such paved areas there; if on the south side, they will bounce sun heat back into the house. A grass area there, on the other hand, adds some actual as well as visual coolness.

LEAVE ROOM TO EXPAND. Even if you don't plan any additions on your vacation home now, unforeseen circumstances may make them desirable later. Therefore it's as well to locate the house so that it could be enlarged at some future time. (This might be a decisive factor with a buyer, in case you later sell). Since land space cannot be added as an afterthought, the question deserves forethought when you orient your house.

Space for sanitation is also vital. Outside toilets of any kind, septic tanks and garbage pits must be at least 100' away from any well or spring supplying drinking water, and also a reasonable distance from the main roadway or path to the house. Such sources of possible contamination should also be downgrade with respect to any flow of underground water, but the slope of the surface is not a reliable gauge, for ground or spring water may flow "uphill" contrary to the topsoil contour. Also, either drought or heavy rainfall may cause such fluctuation of the water level that pollution may back up to the water source. Therefore the drinking water should be checked regularly by a county or state health authority, or disinfected as explained in a later chapter.

In clearing your building site, try to preserve its natural appearance as far as possible. Let those trees stand that do not impede construction or delivery of materials. Avoid trimming off lower branches. Leave brush and shrubbery that is not in itself unsightly or in the way until the structure is up. You will then be better able to judge its effect, and where to transplant greenery to screen the house from the road or from neighbors, or to conceal the foundation. Do, however, clear away deadwood and stumps. If left around, these offer ideal living quarters to termites, which subsequently may find their way to the house.

SETTING OUT BUILDING LINES. Having decided where and how the house is to stand, you must set out fixed reference marks. These should outline the foundation, establish its true and level height, and lay out right angles between adjacent sides of the house.

From 2-by-2 stock, cut four stakes and drive a copper or aluminum tack into the top of each. You will also need some 1-by-4s and builder's line. Drive a stake well into the ground where one corner of the structure is to be. With a steel tape, measure the length of the house and drive a second stake at the far corner. By sighting on landmarks, or with a compass, check the direction and location of these stakes, which represent the front or back of your house. When satisfied, measure the width of the end walls and drive in two more stakes. By eye and with a compass, do your best to place these to form a right angle with the base line.

From the 1-by-4s, cut stakes and boards to build a right-angled frame like that shown in Fig. 3. Drive one of these into the ground a few feet outside each corner stake. Take care to set up all the horizontal boards (batter boards) at exactly the same height. For a small structure, this may be done by using a level on one edge of a long, straightedged board. (In selecting such a board, sight along both edges. Any curvature will show up.)

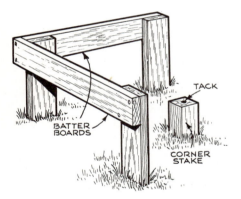

BATTER BOARDS

TACK

CORNER STAKE

Fig. 3. Right-angle frame of batter boards for setting out building lines.

A water level is more accurate (Fig. 4). It requires a length of garden hose without end fittings, two glass tubes 8″ long (such as boiler water glasses) and a funnel. Fit one glass tube to each end of the hose, using tape to form a watertight joint. Insert the funnel in one glass tube and tie this tube alongside a batter board which has been driven into the ground at the desired height of the foundation.

Holding the other tube where another batter board is to be leveled, have someone slowly pour water into the hose until it stands in the first glass at the height of the batter board. It will then stand at precisely the same height in the other tube, which can be carried to each of the other three corners in turn.

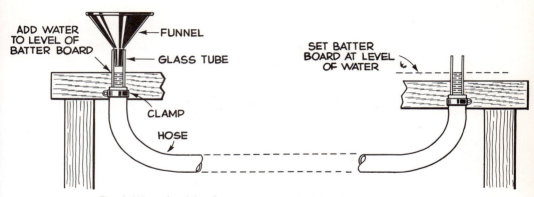

Fig. 4. Water level for determining exact height of batter boards.

Next, stretch lines across the batter boards, holding them with weights, so that they cross exactly over the tacks in the original location stakes. Drop a plumb bob from where the lines intersect, moving them until it hangs directly over the tack (Fig. 5).

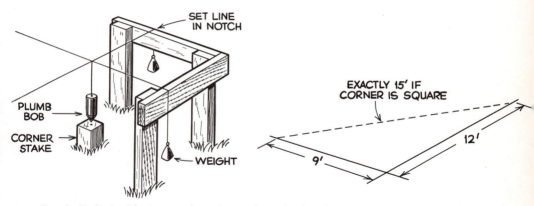

Fig. 5. Method of laying out lines for marking the foundation and checking angles.

The angles between walls are next checked. Measure 9′ from a corner stake along one line, and 12′ from the same stake along the adjacent line. Tie bits of cord at the measured points. Then measure the diagonal distance between these marks. It will be exactly 15′ if—and only if—the two lines form a true 90-degree angle.

The chances are they won't. If the measurement is less than 15′, one line must be moved out; if it is more, one line must be moved in. If satisfied with the orientation of your base line, you will of course adjust the end-wall line, and reset the appropriate corner stake to suit. Proceed to check all the other corners this way, resetting the stakes as you go.

When all four have been checked, make doubly sure by measuring diagonally from opposite corners. The two distances should be equal. If they are not, two or more corners are not true right angles. When satisfied, cut notches in the batter boards under the lines. You can then remove the corner stakes and lines for excavating, but be sure to leave the batter boards. They make it possible to relocate the house lines, by dropping them into the notches you've cut, as a guide in building foundations and walls.

The time and care spent in laying out building lines accurately is worth while. Any error allowed to stand is sure to crop up later.

THE IMPORTANCE OF A FOUNDATION. Most kinds of untreated wood laid directly on the ground decay sooner or later, unless termites find it first. Moisture stands between the wood and the soil, creating ideal conditions for decay fungi. Termites, which shun daylight, can enter freely where wood is in contact with the ground, and there are a number of other insects hardly less destructive. The dampness that persists under the floor of a structure built too close to the ground also gives the place a dank feel and odor.

With the notable exception of a pole house (see Chapter 6), masonry or other supports should be used to lift the bottom wall members (sills) off the ground. Such foundations may be continuous—that is, the full length of the walls—or merely piers located at the corners and at intervals between to prevent sagging of the structure.

The simplest pier, practical only if it can be placed on firm soil or rock, consists of at least two flat stones (Fig. 6). One thick stone won't do because moisture will creep over its surface and reach the wood; the separation between two stones forms an effective barrier. Tamp the bottom stone down hard, turning the upper until it rests solidly on the lower one. Do not cement the stones together, as the filled joint would permit moisture to rise.

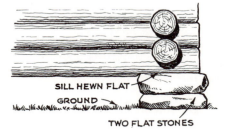

Fig. 6. Two flat stones used as pier foundation for log cabin.

SILL HEWN FLAT
GROUND
TWO FLAT STONES

TREATING WOODEN PIERS. Cedar, cypress, locust or redwood, which have some natural resistance to insect infestation and decay, are sometimes used as foundation piers. Even these woods, however, are not half as durable as stone or masonry. Any other woods sunk into the ground should certainly be treated with coal-tar creosote or a chemical wood preservative. In fact, such treatment will extend the life even of naturally decay-resistant species.

In some areas you can buy pretreated piers, fence posts, sills and other kinds of building lumber. There are also ways in which you can treat wood yourself, although all are tedious, time-consuming and, if they are to be effective, demanding. Proprietary wood preservatives come with instructions, which should be carefully followed. Pentachlorophenol and copper naphthenate are fairly effective, as is that old stand-by, coal-tar creosote. This may be applied in several ways.

Hot Brushing. Heat creosote over an outdoor fire until very hot but short of boiling (about 200 deg. Fahr.). As creosote will catch fire if it boils over, this should be done at a safe distance from trees and underbrush. With a big brush or soft-bristled broom, work two coats well into the wood, filling all cracks and holes. Let the first coat dry before applying the next.

Cold Brushing. Thin creosote with an equal volume of No. 2 fuel oil, so that it can more readily penetrate at air temperature. Apply at least two coats, letting the first one dry before putting on the second.

Cold Soaking. Stand the wood in an oil barrel with a half-and-half mixture of creosote and No. 2 fuel oil, or a 5-percent solution of pentachlorophenol in fuel oil. Let it soak for several days (longer will do no harm). If short pieces are to be treated throughout, turn them upside down in the barrel, and let them stand an equal length of time.

Hot-Cold Method. More difficult because it requires attention for several hours, this consists of soaking the wood in hot creosote for up to twelve hours, followed by soaking in oil-thinned cold creosote for several days.

MAKING PIER FOUNDATIONS. Wooden piers should be about 1′ in diameter and extend about 3′ below ground. Dig the hole to depth, lay a flat stone or a 2″ layer of coarse gravel at the bottom of it, tamp this tight with the pier, and fill around the pier with other stones and gravel, tamping this hard also. Take care to set all the piers with their tops at the same level, using the lines over the batter boards to check this.

Masonry piers should be sunk below the frost line, or the depth to which the ground freezes in winter. If they are set above this, ground action or "heaving" can crack the masonry, lift walls, or even shift the structure. The frost line varies widely in different parts of the country and even within the same state. Ask your materials dealer or local builders how deep it is in the locality where you wish to build. (If you can rest the foundation on solid rock or a dense stratum of underground gravel, all the better.)

To build concrete piers, dig each hole about 2′ square to below frost line. If the sills are to be placed only a few inches above grade (ground level), build an open box of 1-by-12 boards held together by a removable frame as in Fig. 7. Sink it just far enough into the hole to keep concrete from escaping around it.

Though not absolutely necessary, reinforcing rods will strengthen the piers and help protect them from cracking in severe frost. Stick at least four ¾″ steel reinforcing bars into the soil at the bottom of the hole. Join them with diagonal cross rods, wired to the vertical ones about 12″ apart. Mix concrete as described farther on in this chapter. Make sure, in pouring, that it fills every part of the hole and surrounds each reinforcing rod. Place damp sacking on top to prevent premature drying.

The rods may be cut long enough to protrude at the top, the sills later being bored to fit over them, but it is better to insert ¾″ by 12″ bolts head

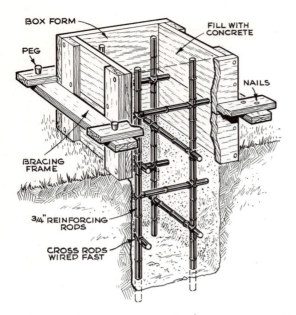

BOX FORM

FILL WITH CONCRETE

PEG

NAILS

BRACING FRAME

3/4" REINFORCING RODS

CROSS RODS WIRED FAST

Fig. 7. Wooden box with removable frame for pouring concrete piers below the frost line.

down in the concrete, with only enough protruding to pass through the sills. These, bored to fit over the bolts, can later be secured with washers and nuts.

Although low piers are sometimes used, the sills should ideally be 18" to 24" above the ground. The latter provides more crawl space and ventilation under the floor. Higher concrete piers can be poured in two stages, the first in a hole 2' square. Insert extra reinforcing rods long enough to protrude well into the second stage. Pour the base or footing within 6" of ground level. While it is still soft, scratch the top surface so that it will bond well with the second stage, and let it set firm.

From 1" lumber, build a form for the upper part to the desired height, smaller but similar to that in Fig. 7. Block this in place with stones. Wet the top of the footing. Then tamp in concrete, working large pieces of the aggregate (gravel or pebbles) well below the surface. Set in sill bolts if desired. Keep the concrete moist six or seven days for proper curing. Such a high pier is shown in Fig. 8.

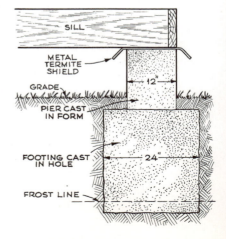

SILL

METAL TERMITE SHIELD

GRADE

PIER CAST IN FORM

12"

FOOTING CAST IN HOLE

24"

FROST LINE

Fig. 8. Concrete pier poured on footing cast beneath ground.

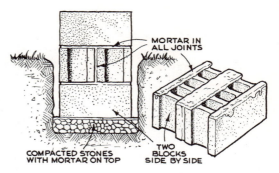

Fig. 9. Double set of concrete blocks used to form square pier at corners.

MORTAR IN ALL JOINTS

COMPACTED STONES WITH MORTAR ON TOP

TWO BLOCKS SIDE BY SIDE

Concrete blocks can be used as piers if solidly set on a footing of concrete, large gravel or stone. The latter two should be so compacted by tamping that the material will not sink farther under load. At corners, blocks may be set double to form a square pier (Fig. 9). Intermediate piers may be single-block width.

Set blocks in a bed of mortar made by mixing one part Portland cement with five of sand and one part hydrated lime. Use only enough water to make a workable mortar. Set the blocks with the openings on top and bottom, not on the sides.

Mortar is also used to make stone piers, but these require a good supply of suitable stones and considerable patience and skill to fit them.

Be sure to wet down both concrete blocks and stones thoroughly before applying the mortar to them. This will prevent the porous masonry from soaking water out of the mortar, and so depriving it of the moisture required for it to set properly.

CONTINUOUS FOUNDATION WALLS cost more than piers and are more difficult to build, but they provide more uniform support and longer life for the house. They are not worth their extra cost and trouble if they are made too thin, or if set on soft soil or inadequate footings. Also, the large amount of concrete needed requires renting a power mixer or delivery by a transit-mix truck. Rather than skimp on a continuous foundation, you may do better to build substantial piers.

If you do want a foundation wall, cast footings must extend below the frost line and should be at least 8″ wider than the walls proper. Dig a trench to cast the footings in, making the bottom corners square. Dubbed off or rounded corners lessen the load capacity. In soft soil, make the footings more than 8″ wider than the walls, or dig down to denser soil or gravel. Clean out loose soil from the trench and, if the soil is dry, wet it with a fine spray before pouring concrete.

For foundation walls of concrete blocks or fieldstone, smooth the top of the footing level. For cast foundation walls, bevel the sides of a 2-by-4, brush on old crankcase oil, and press it into the footing while the mix is still soft to form a rebate or key slot (Fig. 10).

Keep the cast footing moist several days. When it has set hard, remove the 2-by-4 and set up forms for casting the walls. To leave ventilating open-

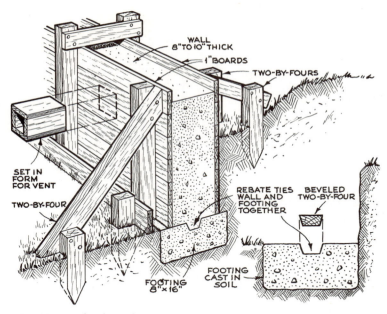

Fig. 10. Wooden forms for casting continuous foundation wall on footing.

ings, which are vital in any closed foundation, nail boxlike frames between the forms, as shown in Fig. 10, every 6 to 8 feet. (A cellar wall, with normal door and window openings, would not require such ventilating holes, which should be screened eventually to keep out small animals.) Wet the footing thoroughly before casting the wall on top of it.

Foundations for log cabins should be built with the end walls half a log higher than the side walls to allow for the manner in which the logs are laid up. The U.S. Department of Agriculture recommends that concrete foundation walls be about 3″ thicker than the logs to be used for the cabin.

In stone foundation walls, some stones should be the full width of the wall, and there should be at least one of these to every 8 square feet of wall surface. Do not let the mortar joints form continuous lines, which may allow cracks to extend. Instead, stagger joints all through the wall. Remember to leave ventilating holes at frequent intervals, bridging them with long stones at the top.

THE SLAB FOUNDATION. If you are going to build on firm, well-drained ground, you might consider the popular slab foundation, which can form the floor as well as the support for the structure. Adequate drainage is very important because the floor is close to the ground (although it should be at least 6″ above it). Being comparatively thin, the slab must have heavier footings where it is to bear the load of walls and roof. It should also have a well-compacted granular fill under it for drainage and insulation below the floor area.

In excavating for a slab, remove all roots and organic refuse from the area, which should be leveled and then tamped firm. Around it, dig trenches below the frost line for footings under the outer walls and any load-bearing

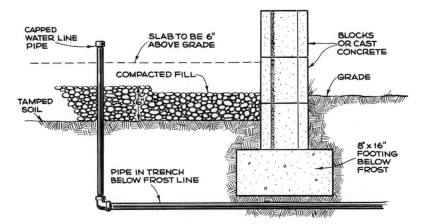

Fig. 11. First stage in building a slab foundation showing footings and piers in place, pipes laid below frost line, and layer of compacted fill.

partitions (inside walls that help support the roof). Foundation walls above the footings may be cast or laid up of concrete blocks (Fig. 11).

Dig trenches below the frost line for any water or waste pipes that are to run under the floor. Lay these pipes, carry the ends up above slab height, and cap them.

The footings can now be cast. Because of the large amount of concrete needed, it is most practical to buy it premixed for delivery by truck. Be sure that all forms (if any), pipes and electrical conduit to be embedded in the foundation are in place before the concrete arrives, as pouring cannot be delayed.

Pour and compact a coarse gravel fill to a depth of 6″ in the floor area, except for an 18″ width around the edges, where it may be 5″ to allow for insulation. Pour a thin layer of 1-to-3 cement-and-sand mix over the fill to form a surface for waterproofing. When this has set, swab on hot asphalt, followed by asphalt-saturated roofing felt, another coating of hot asphalt, and a second layer of felt, well overlapped at the edges (Fig. 12).

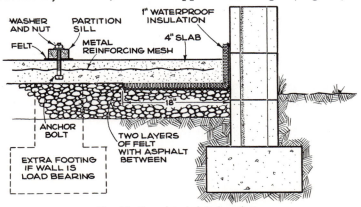

Fig. 12. Completed slab foundation.

Carry the second layer of felt up the footing walls a little above floor height. For winter occupancy, it's well to lay a strip of 1″ waterproof insulation along the walls and up to slab height.

Mark this height along the walls at various points, using a level. Pour concrete to about 2½″ depth, spade and level it, and lay on metal reinforcing mesh made for the purpose. Then pour more concrete to a total slab depth of 4″ or more. Smooth with a leveling board and a wood float.

Anchor bolts for partitions may be set into the soft concrete. If you want a wood floor over the slab (which is optional) you can set in anchoring clips to tie the floor to the slab. Finish smoothing the surface with a steel trowel and, as with any concrete work, keep it moist for several days to cure properly.

If a slab foundation is used on poorly drained ground, drain tile should be laid around the footing to lead off subsoil water. Do this before backfilling around the slab. The tile (actually a ceramic pipe) is not joined tightly; a small gap is left between adjacent pieces (Fig. 13). Each section must slope toward a common low point from which water can drain down a hillside, into a gully, sewer system or dry well. The latter may be simply a bottomless barrel sunk into the ground, filled with stones, and covered so that soil won't clog the stone fill when the barrel is buried.

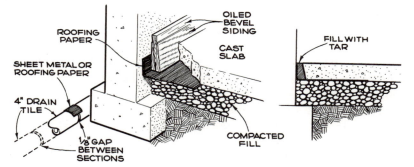

Fig. 13. Drain tile leads off subsoil water on poorly drained ground; waterproof joint between slab and footing protects against seepage.

The ⅛″ gaps between drain-tile sections must be similarly protected with sheet metal, roofing paper or pieces of composition shingle before backfilling is done.

Protection against seepage can also be provided by a waterproof joint between slab and footing, as shown in Fig. 13. Oil three lengths of bevel siding and place them against the wall with the thick edge of the center piece up and that of the other two down. After the slab has set, pry up the middle piece, remove the other two also, and fill the wedge-shaped gap with hot tar or roofing compound.

HOW TO MAKE GOOD CONCRETE. How strong, lasting and watertight concrete will be depends on the amount of water mixed in it. Although at one time concrete mixes were specified as so much cement, sand and gravel, with an unspecified amount of water left to the user's judgment, the modern way is to specify the volume of water and even to take into account the dampness or wetness of sand and aggregate used in the mix. The accompanying chart, reproduced by permission of the Portland Cement Association, shows typical mixes and how the correct proportion of water may vary. Too much water weakens the bonding qualities of the cement.

Kind of work	Gal. of water added to each 1-sack batch if sand is:			Suggested mixture for 1-sack trial batches			Materials per cu. yd. of concrete *				
	Damp¹	Wet² (average sand)	Very wet³	Cement, sacks (cu. ft.)	Aggregates Fine cu. ft.	Coarse cu. ft.	Cement sacks	Aggregates Fine cu. ft.	lb.	Coarse cu. ft.	lb.
5 gal. of water per sack of cement (1: 2: 2¼ mix)											
Concrete subjected to severe wear, weather, or weak acid and alkali solutions *(Maximum size aggregate 1½ in.)*	4½	4	3½	1	2	2¼	7¾	15½	1400	17½	1750
6 gal. of water per sack of cement (1: 2¼: 3 mix)											
Floors (such as home, basement, dairy barn), driveways, walks, septic tanks, storage tanks, structural beams, columns and slabs *(Maximum size aggregate 1 in.)*	5½	5	4¼	1	2¼	3	6¼	14	1260	19	1900
7 gal. of water per sack of cement (1: 3: 4 mix)											
Foundation walls, footings, mass concrete, etc. *(Maximum size aggregate 1½ in.)*	6¼	5½	4¾	1	3	4	5	15	1350	20	2000

¹ *Damp* describes sand which will fall apart after being squeezed in the palm of the hand.

² *Wet* describes sand which will ball in the hand when squeezed but leaves no moisture on the palm.

³ *Very Wet* describes sand that has been subjected to a recent rain or recently pumped. Balling a sample in the hand will leave moisture on the palm and the sand-gravel glistens in the light.

* No allowance for waste.

The trial batches suggested should be made in small quantities to test the suitability of the mix for the work in hand. If the mix proves to be too wet, add small quantities of sand or pebbles. If it is too stiff, reduce the amounts of sand and pebbles in next trial batch. *Do not change the amount of water.*

Too much sand makes concrete porous and reduces the amount you can make with a sack of cement. Too much aggregate (gravel or pebbles) makes concrete hard to work and finish. The right amount of cement-sand mortar will fill the spaces between the aggregate and can be troweled to a smooth surface on top.

Not all sand is suitable for concrete; it should be clean, well graded, with particles of varying size, and free of organic material, loam and clay. Gravel should be a mixture of fine and coarse particles and free of sand. Water must be clean and uncontaminated by alkali, acid or oil.

A pail can be used for measuring small quantities. For larger amounts, remember that a sack of cement holds exactly 1 cubic foot. A box measure can be built to hold 1 or 2 cubic feet of sand or aggregate.

Although small amounts can be mixed in a metal wheelbarrow, a mixing floor should be available for larger quantities. A platform of matched (tongued and grooved) lumber or two sheets of waterproof plywood will serve. Put down the measured sand, then the cement, and mix these thoroughly to a uniform gray color, free of streaks that indicate unmixed material. Spread the measured aggregate on top and mix until it is uniformly distributed. Pour the measured amount of water into a depression in the middle of the pile and continue mixing to a uniform consistency. Pour within thirty minutes. Cover with earth, straw, canvas or burlap and keep moist by sprinkling for about seven days.

CHAPTER SIX

A SIMPLE POLE CABIN AND CARPORT

For the vacationer who wants to build quickly and at a low cost, this attractive little cabin has much to recommend it. Some of its unusual features seem at first to contradict points made in preceding chapters. It has, for example, no foundation. It is literally built into the ground. There is no floor, and as a fishing or hunting retreat on a well-located site it may be left without one.

The living area is 10′ by 12′ and the carport, suitable for a small car, the same size. As shown in the plans, which are used by courtesy of Masonite Corporation, the structure was built in two weekends.

Attractive pole cabin with carport combines low cost and structural simplicity.

Despite its low cost and simple construction, the cabin will be reasonably durable if treated lumber is used where specified. The addition of a floor, as shown farther on, need not be expensive.

There are other options you may choose to exercise. Headroom is modest, and might well be increased slightly if the occupants are to be six-footers. For much less than double the cost, you could enclose the carport area as well and have twice the living space. To shelter a standard-size automobile, a roof extension could be added to the carport section either in front or in back. The basic construction could be adapted to your own design, provided you maintain the same spacing of crucial framing members—poles, rafters and girts.

Even if a floor is added, it will be close to the ground. For the comfort of the occupants, it is highly important that the site should be dry and well drained, with no standing water at any time. If possible, locate on a rise so that ground water will at no time flow toward the cabin.

CONSTRUCTING THE FRAME. Two lengths of 4″ poles are needed, eight of them 12′ long for the outer walls, and three 14′ long under the roof ridge. All of these, and the 2-by-6 tongue-and-groove stock forming the bottom frame, must be impregnated with pentachlorophenol (penta-treated) to meet Federal Specification TTW-571.

It is much easier and more satisfactory to buy such lumber pretreated than to try to treat it yourself. Building with untreated material would be poor economy, for the structure would eventually deteriorate from the ground up.

Use only galvanized or otherwise rustproofed nails. These will go far toward eliminating rust spots and the loosening of joints, especially at ground level and in the roof structure. Ringed, spiral-thread and screw nails grip more securely than ordinary ones and repay their extra cost in durability.

Set out the post-hole locations with stakes and line, using the triangular method of ensuring right-angled corners as explained in Chapter 5. Note that all dimensions are to the outside of the framing (Fig. 1). Dig the holes about 8″ in diameter and fully 3′ deep. A post-hole digger is almost indispensable; digging with a spade is much more difficult and leaves bell-mouthed holes that do not grip posts as securely. You can rent such a tool if you don't own one.

Drop in the four corner posts of the living area—two 12′ and two 14′ poles. If only one end of the posts is treated, be sure it's this that goes into the ground.

Dig a shallow trench (about 6″ deep) around the perimeter of the four poles. Place two 10′ and two 12′ lengths of penta-treated, 2-by-6 tongue-and-groove lumber outside the corner poles. Nail these pieces together like a frame, check it for squareness, and level it in the trench. Its top edge should be at ground level. Don't nail it to the poles as yet, but stake it in position.

Now assemble the two 20′ end plates, a 12′ center girt, and two 12′ rafter plates right on top of the staked bottom frame (Fig. 2). Nail the upper frame together with diagonal braces across the corners to hold it square.

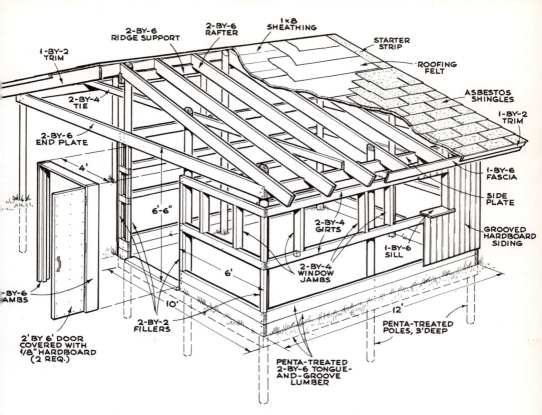

Fig. 1. Overall plan of pole cabin showing dimensions and all framing members.

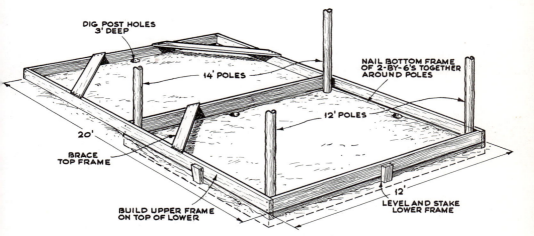

Fig. 2. Method of setting up corner posts and sinking lower frame into trench. Note: Upper frame rests *temporarily* on lower prior to being raised.

Then turn the poles with their best sides outward and nail the *lower* frame securely to them.

Measure exactly 6'6" up from the top of the bottom frame at the corner poles, driving a nail part way in at each mark. With a helper, lift the upper plate frame into position against the marker nails and nail it firmly to the poles.

Drop all the other poles into their holes. Carefully plumb the corner poles, nailing braces from them to the inside of the bottom frame. Plumb and brace the remaining poles to stakes if necessary.

Now add the other tongue-and-groove girts, driving them firmly against the bottom one. In the front wall, use 5′ lengths to span the distance from the corner to the door post, and lay another 5′ length as a door sill, nailing it to the bottom piece and to the poles.

Backfill soil against the bottom frame, tamping it hard at frequent intervals as you shovel it into the trench. A short log or a piece of railway tie with wooden handles nailed on makes a practical tamper.

The 2-by-4 girts that frame the windows and support the siding may now be nailed to the poles. See that they are level and the same distance apart their full lengths. At the corner and door poles, fit 2-by-2 vertical fillers between the girts to form a square nailing surface for the siding and door frame.

BUILDING THE ROOF. Level the 2-by-6 ridge support at a height of 9′6″ and nail it to the three center poles. Use a framing square to calculate rafter angles as explained in Chapter 8, or temporarily nail a 1-by-6 across the ridge support and a side plate. Scribe the angle cuts and notches on this. The lower ends of the rafters are left square. Cut and notch the 1-by-6 this way, making any necessary corrections after trying it in place. When it fits, use it as a pattern to cut the rafters.

Toenail the rafters to the ridge support and plates. Also nail the end and center rafters to the poles alongside which they lie. Across the third rafter from each end place a 20′ 2-by-4 tie, resting it on the side plates and nailing it to both the plates and the rafters. Finally, saw all the poles flush with the top edges of the rafters.

Nail 1-by-6 fascia boards to the ends of all the rafters on each side. These boards are 14′ long and so will extend 1′ beyond the end rafters at front and back (Fig. 3).

Now put on the 1-by-8 roof sheathing. Twenty-one boards, also 14′ long, are used for each half of the roof. Nail 12′ fascia boards to the gable ends of the sheathing. Then apply 1-by-2 trim all around.

Lay 15-pound roofing felt parallel to the sheathing boards, starting at the bottom edge of the roof and working up. A starter strip of asbestos roofing is then nailed along the gable edges, and finally asbestos shingles are applied, the first course being laid at the eaves so that succeeding ones always overlap, with a ridge cap at the peak.

FITTING DOORS AND WINDOWS. Frame the window openings with 2-by-4s to fit purchased casement or sliding windows. The framing, placed with its 4″ dimension at right angles to the girts, should be notched to make its outer edge flush with the surface of the girts (see Fig. 1).

Nail the door frame to the poles and fillers, and nail door stops inside the

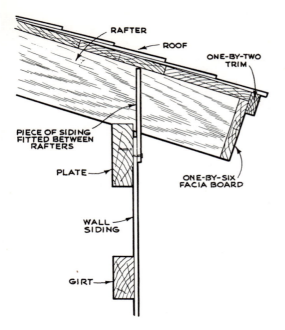

RAFTER

ROOF

ONE-BY-TWO TRIM

PIECE OF SIDING FITTED BETWEEN RAFTERS

PLATE

ONE-BY-SIX FACIA BOARD

WALL SIDING

GIRT

Fig. 3. Cross-section of roof showing rafters resting on side plate, with facia board nailed to ends. Siding fits between rafters.

frame. Use blocks to fill any gaps between the frame and poles. If you wish to frame a smaller door, nail 2-by-4s vertically between the end plate and sill, the required distance apart. Fit blocks between these and the poles for extra rigidity.

Used doors can save you money. Covering both sides with ⅛″ Masonite tempered Presdwood will strengthen them and greatly improve their appearance.

APPLY SIDING IN PANEL FORM. Hardboard siding such as Masonite Panelgroove adds strength to the structure by bracing the framing. It goes up quickly, is highly durable, and takes any oil-base house paint. These $\frac{5}{16}$″ panels come either with smooth surfaces between the grooves, or with an attractive striated surface. Their edges are rabbeted and automatically fit together to make invisible joints.

The siding is applied with the grooves vertical. Saw individual panels to length and place them in position to scribe window openings along the girts and jambs. Cut these out; then fasten the siding in position with 8d galvanized box nails. Don't use casing or finishing nails, which have smaller heads. Place nails 4″ apart at panel edges, 8″ apart within the panels. At joints, put the next overlapping panel in place and nail through both flange thicknesses as in Fig. 4. Apply calking compound to window and door frames where the siding is to be butted against them.

To close the openings in the eaves above the side plates, cut 9″ or 10″ siding to lengths that will fit snugly between the rafters. With the wall siding up, push these pieces into position so that they overlap the panel below, and nail them along the bottom edge to the plate and panel as shown in Fig. 3.

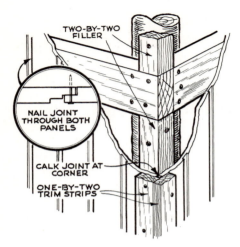

TWO-BY-TWO FILLER

NAIL JOINT THROUGH BOTH PANELS

CALK JOINT AT CORNER

ONE-BY-TWO TRIM STRIPS

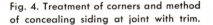

Fig. 4. Treatment of corners and method of concealing siding at joint with trim.

Plug any small openings with calking or screening to keep out birds, insects and rodents.

At the corners, cover the siding with two 1-by-2 strips, closely butted their full length and with calking underneath (Fig. 4). Notch window sills to fit around and extend a little beyond the jambs. Install them with a downward slope to drain water toward the outside. Use 1-by-2 strips for window and door trim.

FINISHING THE CABIN. Panelgroove siding can be bought with a prime coat applied at the factory. This is not a finish coat, and should be painted within sixty days after installation. If it is exposed longer, or you buy unprimed Panelgroove, apply a coat of good exterior linseed-oil base primer. Finish with two coats of any good linseed-oil exterior house paint (alkyd, latex and other synthetic-base paints are not recommended). An attractive two-tone effect results from painting the wood trim a contrasting color.

Laying the Floor. The simplest floor is one of duckboards, made of wooden members nailed to cleats. A smoother, warmer floor that is also easier to walk

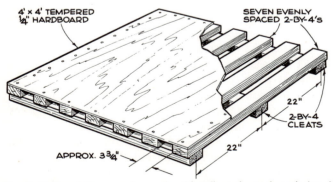

4' x 4' TEMPERED ¼" HARDBOARD

SEVEN EVENLY SPACED 2-BY-4'S

22"

2-BY-4 CLEATS

APPROX. 3¾"

22"

Fig. 5. Optional floor can be made of hardboard panels nailed to frame of 2-by-4s.

on can be made of panels of Masonite ¼″ tempered Presdwood fastened to a framework of 2-by-4s as shown in Fig. 5.

Plane or sandpaper the edges of the 4′-by-4′ panels to a bevel that will form a groove line where panels meet. Then moisten the screen-textured side of the panels with water, using a brush or broom. Stack them with the wet sides together, cover with a drop cloth or tarpaulin, and let them stand at least twenty-four hours. Then wipe off excess moisture and nail them to the frames with 2d cement-coated casing nails spaced 6″ apart along the edges and at least ⅜″ inside them. Inside the panel, nail spacing may be 12″.

Level the soil over the floor area. Lay 55-pound roll roofing on it, overlapping the asphaltum-coated edges of each strip generously and carrying the material up the walls for about 3″. The floor panels are then laid on this. See that they lie flat without tilting or shake. Leave a small gap between adjacent panels; don't force any together.

Where the poles intrude on the floor area, make panels with the cleats set in 5″ from the edge to be placed against the wall. Cut one or two of the crosspieces short or notch them around the pole. Make a semicircular notch in the hardboard panel to fit around the pole as in Fig. 6.

With such solid floor panels, it is wise to provide ventilation under the floor. Bore 2″ holes in the second tongue-and-groove girt about 6′ apart. Nail screening over these inside the wall, or bore the holes to a snug fit for small louvered vents (Fig. 6).

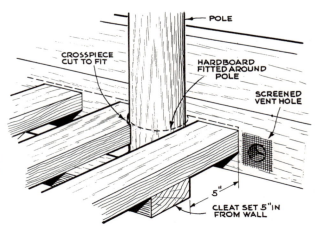

Fig. 6. Hardboard fitted around pole and screened vent hole between cleats.

LIST OF MATERIALS

8—4″ x 12′ penta treated poles*
3—4″ x 14′ penta treated poles*
6—2″ x 6″ x 12′ penta treated T&G lumber*
6—2″ x 6″ x 10′ penta treated T&G lumber*
4—2″ x 6″ x 12′ rafter plates & girts
14—2″ x 6″ x 12′ rafters
2—2″ x 6″ x 20′ end plates
2—2″ x 4″ x 20′ ties

2—⅛″ x 4′ x 6′ Masonite door covering
2—2 x 6 doors
1—Roll 15# asphalt felt
3½—Squares asbestos shingles
2—4″ x 12′ Masonite siding
4—4″ x 10′ Masonite siding
4—4″ x 8′ Masonite siding
2—4″ x 8′ 1¼″ Peg Board

1—2" x 4" x 14' window jambs
8—2" x 4" x 12' girts
2—2" x 4" x 10' girts
1—1" x 6" x 16' door frame
3—1" x 6" x 14' window sill & fascia
4—1" x 6" x 12' fascia on gable
1—16' R.E. door stop
1—1" x 3" x 16' door trim
2—1" x 3" x 14' trim window
5—1" x 3" x 12' trim window, corner trim
2—1" x 2" x 16' roof trim & corner trim
42—1" x 8" x 14' sheathing for roof boards
6—1" x 2" x 12' roof trim & corner trim

Hardware
16d nails, ringed 6#
8d galv. nails 4#
8d common nails 15#
Required roofing nails
6—3½" x 3½" butt hinges
Door handles

Utility Windows
2—6 Lt. 2' x 3' 11"
1—6 Lt. 2' 4" x 2' 1"

* Penta treated materials should meet Federal Specification TTW-571.

CHAPTER SEVEN

BUILDING THE TRUE LOG CABIN

To BUILD with real logs is by no means the easiest nor necessarily the cheapest way to construct even a simple hunting or fishing lodge. Whether to use logs will depend first of all on their availability, and secondly on the time and effort you are willing to expend. The preparation of fresh-cut logs is a big factor in this. In addition to the labor of felling (and perhaps peeling) them, you must allow at least six months for proper seasoning.

A possible short-cut around this delay is to buy peeled and seasoned logs, or used poles from a telephone or untility company. If you have no timber on your own land or cannot legally cut trees down (as is usually the case in national or state forests), ask local residents, feed and farm-machinery dealers whether they know of anyone who has logs to sell or trees to be cleared.

This one-room cabin built of peeled logs blends with its wooded surroundings. Foundation walls of rock slabs support the sills, from which the log walls are built up with saddle notches at the corners. The extended eaves provide a roof for the porch. *U.S. Forest Service.*

Built on concrete-and-rock piers, this more elaborate cabin also utilizes peeled logs saddle notched at the corners. Gable ends are closed with boards and battens, which are also used to enclose the extra wing. An exterior stone chimney is decorative and in keeping with the rustic design. *U.S. Forest Service.*

Pre-cut log cabins are available complete with all wall, roof and floor materials, partitioning, doors and windows, hardware and trim. This cabin, built of vertical white-cedar half logs splined together, comes with full plans and instructions. It can be erected by almost any person with a basic knowledge of tools. *Courtesy Mohawk Log Cabin, Inc.*

The best logs for cabin construction are cedar, redwood, bald cypress, pine, fir and larch. Almost any species can be used, but woods of low decay resistance such as aspen, hemlock and cottonwood must be treated with creosote or other preservative promptly after cutting.

Logs from 4" in diameter and up can be used for cabins, the smaller ones for roof rafters. For wall logs to be laid horizontally, the best sizes are 10" to 12". These should have as little taper as possible to avoid extra chinking or laborious hand hewing. Lengths of 20′ are about the maximum for easy handling, a point to remember in planning the structure if help is limited. Remember that interlocked corners require logs about 2′ longer than the walls themselves. Joining shorter lengths, though feasible, takes extra work and weakens the walls.

PEELED VS. UNPEELED LOGS. Bark left on logs slows down their drying so much that some wood decay is likely before seasoning is complete. Bark also harbors some insects that ultimately damage the log. If you do wish to use unpeeled logs for building, they should be cut in winter and stacked off the ground at once to promote drying. The Forest Products Laboratory of the U.S. Forest Service recommends spraying or brushing on a protective chemical as soon as possible. A solution of 0.5 percent of the gamma isomer of benzene hexachloride (preferably the odorless form) and 2 to 3 percent of pentachlorophenol in light oil (such as No. 2 fuel oil) is said to be effective. Once-a-year spraying of the finished log cabin with this solution is suggested. Caution: treat all wood preservatives as the poisons they are.

If the bark tends to drop off, a narrow strip may be taken off opposite sides of the log for its full length to inhibit peeling. This also promotes faster drying, and the logs can be placed with the scored strips up and down in the cabin walls, so that they will be concealed by the calking. Large pieces of loose bark can be nailed back on, preferably after the logs have dried somewhat.

With the bark off, logs dry faster and are less liable to insect and fungus damage both during and after seasoning. Peeled logs are easier to build with and simpler to maintain. The Forest Products Laboratory recommends that logs to be peeled be cut during the winter, even though the bark is more difficult to strip off then than in spring or summer; less likelihood of insect and decay damage makes the extra effort worth while.

Trim off all limbs, knots and humps when you peel the logs. Stack them on skids, no more than two high, with at least 2″ between adjacent logs, and poles between the layers to promote air circulation (Fig. 1). Place curved logs with the bend upward so that their own weight will straighten them.

3″POLES

TWO-BY-SIX SKIDS

LOGS 2″ APART

Fig. 1. Stacking peeled logs for drying during the winter.

Logs peeled during warm weather may develop blue mold stains, which do no harm but detract from the appearance. To prevent these stains, the Forest Products Laboratory recommends spraying or brushing with a water solution of sodium pentachloride or other preventive within a day after the logs have been peeled.

THE LOG CABIN FOUNDATION. Piers or foundation walls should hold the bottom logs, or sills, 18″ to 24″ above the ground. The end-wall foundations should be half a log higher than sidewall foundations to compensate for half-lap corner joints. With solid foundation walls, remember to leave ventilating openings. The Forest Products Laboratory suggests laying 55-pound or heavier roll roofing on the ground inside the foundation, if the site is damp, to reduce evaporated moisture that fosters decay. Don't enclose a pier foundation permanently; if you do close it for more warmth in winter, remove the boards during other seasons. Lattice screening, of course, will permit adequate ventilation, but don't install it in contact with the ground. It will not only be subject to decay, but may provide an avenue for termites.

These pests won't attack wood properly treated with preservative, so at least the sill logs should be so protected. Metal shields also discourage the entry of termites.

POINTERS ON PLANNING CABINS. Pioneer log cabins, usually glassless and built with an eye to defense, had few windows and those were small ones. Your own cabin will be the better for standard-size casement windows. Low, wide ones harmonize best with the typical one-story structure. The more windows, the fewer logs you will need and the lighter the interior. But they must be strongly framed to avoid weakening walls, and so spaced as to leave ample wall space for bunks and other furnishings.

If you build without an architectural plan, you should at least make a sketch of the cabin layout and its dimensions, which in log construction are usually taken to the inside of the walls. Logs should be laid plumb on the inside. Any slope due to variation in the size of the logs will therefore appear on the outside of the wall (Fig. 2), but this will be explained shortly.

A low, rambling design, with the eaves little higher than the top of the doors, is usually appropriate, whereas short, boxy proportions are unattractive. There are good reasons for a wide roof overhang. (Forest Service authorities recommend a projection of 18″ to 24″). Besides shielding southern windows from the sun, it keeps a lot of rain off the upper part of the walls and conducts runoff away from the foundation. This helps reduce the likelihood of decay in walls and sills, and around doors and windows.

You may have to utilize some short, crooked or excessively tapered logs. Although experts prefer to lay up walls of long logs and cut doors and windows out afterwards, you can with some extra effort make shorter logs serve for the areas between such openings, saving long logs for use above and below them. Try to use the heaviest logs at the bottom of walls, gradually de-

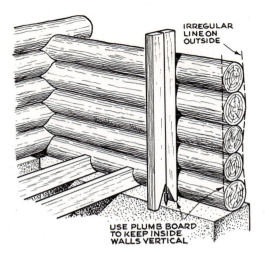

IRREGULAR LINE ON OUTSIDE

USE PLUMB BOARD TO KEEP INSIDE WALLS VERTICAL

Fig. 2. Plumbing inside of log wall.

creasing log diameters toward the top. In typical cross-lap joints used at corners, the lower logs may well project farther than those above.

Try to fit logs as tightly as possible. If it is necessary to trim off a bump or knot, this should if possible always be done on the upper log, the cut surfaces being placed downward for free drainage. A tight fit can be attained by clamping two logs together and running a chain saw between them for their entire length, removing bumps and irregularities on both logs at the same time. Chain-saw manufacturers, incidentally, will provide you with invaluable advice on using the saw for building with logs. If rain-catching crevices cannot be avoided, creosote the wood and calk the opening Remember that water is not harmful so long as it can run off quickly; it is rain that is caught and soaks in that fosters decay.

STARTING LOG WALLS. Construction begins with laying the sills. Choose the soundest, straightest, least tapering logs and dress them flat where they are to rest on the foundation. If you are using sill bolts, bore the sills to fit over them. The bolt holes may be counterbored to sink the nuts flush, or shallow holes can be bored for them in the next log above, so that it can rest firmly on the sill.

Once the side-wall sills are down, it is time to place the joists, or framing members that support the floor. If foundation walls are continuous, either logs 6″ to 8″ in diameter or sawed lumber (2-by-6s for spans to 12′, 2-by-8s for longer joists) may be set on the walls and let into notches cut into the sills as in Fig. 3. The notches require only two cuts apiece, the waste being chiseled out between. Sawed joists should be 16″, logs 18″ apart, measured on centers.

With pier foundations, the joists must rest fully on the sills. A method much used by pioneers is shown in Fig. 4. The joists extend to or beyond the outside of the wall line. Hew both sills and joists slightly flat where they touch for secure seating. Predrill a hole halfway through the joist and drive a 40-penny spike through the joint, using a punch to drive it well into the hole.

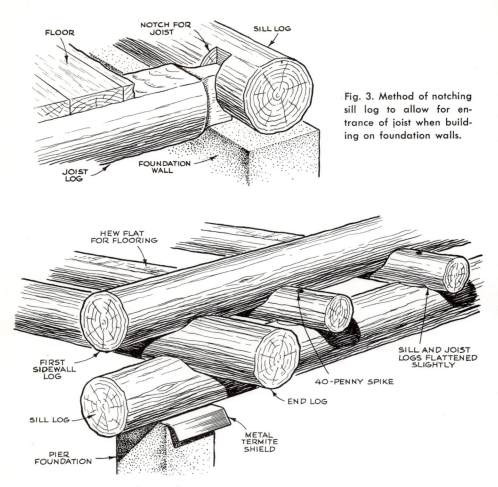

FLOOR

NOTCH FOR JOIST

SILL LOG

Fig. 3. Method of notching sill log to allow for entrance of joist when building on foundation walls.

JOIST LOG

FOUNDATION WALL

HEW FLAT FOR FLOORING

FIRST SIDEWALL LOG

SILL AND JOIST LOGS FLATTENED SLIGHTLY

40-PENNY SPIKE

END LOG

SILL LOG

METAL TERMITE SHIELD

PIER FOUNDATION

Fig. 4. Joists resting fully on sills and extending beyond wall line when building on piers.

Hew the tops of the joists flat, using a stretched line to bring them all to the same level so that the floor boards will lie evenly.

The end-wall logs can be so sized and notched over the sill ends that the next following side-wall log, which goes on top of the end logs, will require little or no notching over the joists.

Another way to frame log joists is to cut tenons on each end, and a corresponding mortise or socket in the sill (Fig. 5). Take care not to notch the underside of the joist tenon too deeply, for it carries the load. Drive a spike into each joint to tie sill and joists securely together. Hew the tops of the joists level with the sills.

To frame sawed joists, you can spike a 2-by-6 to the inside of the sill its full length, and a 2-by-4 inside that, the tops of both members being approximately flush with the top of the sill (Fig. 6). The joists are then toenailed to these ledger strips and to the sills. The upper joist corners may be trimmed slightly to fit around the second side-wall log.

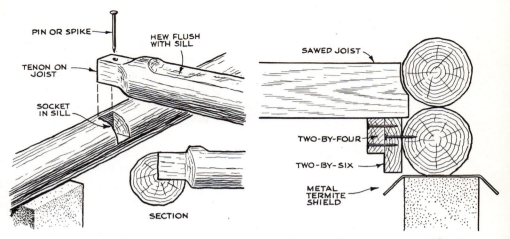

Fig. 5. Mortise-and-tenon joint used to join joists and sills. Joists are hewn flat, spiked to sill.

Fig. 6. Sawed joist resting on 2-by-6 and 2-by-4 nailed to sill.

A better method, which does not depend on spikes to transfer the floor load to the sills, is to notch these as for tenoned log joists. The 2″ sawed joists, however, are not tenoned, but set into the notches to full depth, the second sidewall log also being notched to accommodate them, as shown in Fig. 7. Reinforce sawed floor joists with at least one line of bridging as described in Chapter 8.

LOG CORNER JOINTS. One of the best corner joints is the round-notch or saddle type, in which the upper log is notched to fit over the lower one (Fig. 8D). Moisture drains out of such a joint, it is self-locking, and it is easier to make than some other kinds. U.S. Forest Service bulletin 579 suggests marking out the notches as follows:

Lay the top log in proper alignment across the lower one, securing it with log dogs. Use big dividers with a pencil holder and level bubble attachment for scribing. Set the dividers to half the diameter of the lower log.

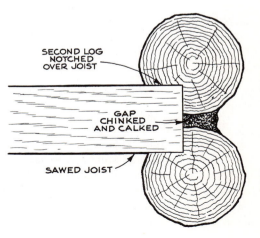

Fig. 7. Sawed joist set into notches cut in both sill and log above.

Touch the lower leg of the dividers to the side of this log with the level bubble up and the pencil touching the underside of the top log as in Fig. 8A. Watching the bubble to keep the divider legs vertical, move the instrument first around the bottom of the upper log and then up the lower log, scribing a quarter circle on the upper one as shown in Fig. 8B. Complete this by scribing from the other side. Then repeat by scribing twice from the other side of the top log, thus outlining the entire notch.

Turn the upper log over, intensify the markings with a carpenter's pencil or chalk, and rough out the notch with an axe or a power saw. Chip out to the mark, using a big gouge chisel for final fitting if necessary. It's desirable to cup out the notch so that the weight of the log rests on the outer edges, making a tighter joint. Mark subsequent notches the same way, setting the dividers to the distance between the top of the under log and the bottom of the next as in Fig. 8C.

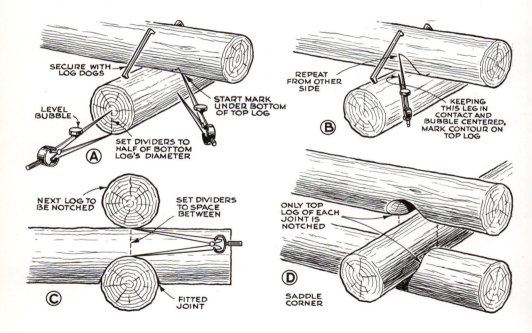

Fig. 8. Scribing round notch in upper log to fit over lower log.

The logs should be spiked together as they are laid. Bore ¾″ holes half way through the upper log and a $7/16$″ hole the rest of the way. Drive in a 10″ spike, using a ⅝″ steel rod to set it to the bottom of the larger hole and halfway into the lower log. Stagger the location of spikes in alternate rounds of logs to avoid interference. Spiking prevents logs from springing out of alignment, and should be done about 2′ from each corner and alongside door and window openings.

The inside face of the logs should be kept plumb. A plumb board is better than a carpenter's level for this, as well as for marking door and window openings. Find a board 6' to 8' long that is of uniform width, with absolutely straight edges. Make a small notch exactly at the center of one end, and saw a deep, precisely centered V-notch at the other end (Fig. 2). Hang a plumb line in the upper notch, with the bob in the lower one, as shown.

As each round of logs is laid, try to keep the corners at approximately the same height. Check this by measuring up from the joists at intervals. You can alter corner height when necessary either by notching more or less deeply, or by turning logs end for end so as to put the heavier butts where height is to be gained.

FRAMING WALL OPENINGS. It is standard procedure to lay logs the full length of all walls (placing bad spots where openings are to be made) and cut window and door openings out afterwards. To keep the location of these in mind during construction, it is a good idea to mark them on the inside of the first round of logs, writing the height of each opening-to-be inside the marks.

To frame a door, a wide notch is cut in the doorsill log to the level of the floor joists, its width being that of the door plus the thickness of both jambs. You can then continue laying logs up to the last one below the top of the opening. Either cut this one away for the full width, or notch it deeply at the outer limits of the opening as in Fig. 9, so that a saw can be passed. through. Using a level or plumb board, nail a 2"-thick board in position temporarily as a sawing guide. You can then use a two-man crosscut saw or a reciprocating-blade power saw to cut through the remaining logs down to the bottom notch. Save the short pieces for use elsewhere.

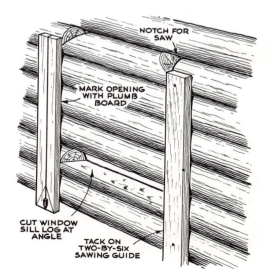

Fig. 9. Cutting window opening with aid of plumbed guides. Note sill log cut at angle sloping towards outside to shed water.

NOTCH FOR SAW

MARK OPENING WITH PLUMB BOARD

CUT WINDOW SILL LOG AT ANGLE

TACK ON TWO-BY-SIX SAWING GUIDE

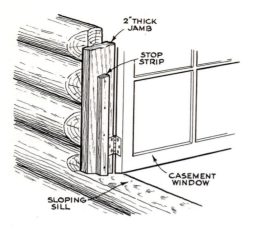

Fig. 10. Installation of casement window, with jamb slightly narrower than sill.

False jambs of sawed 2″ lumber are spiked to each log. You may wish to use jambs slightly narrower than the average log diameter, and trim the log ends at an agle as in Fig. 10. It is wise to apply preservative to the cut ends and the backs of the jambs before you install these.

Cut the sill log in window openings at an angle sloping downward on the outside, so that it sheds water. Saw jamb ends to suit.

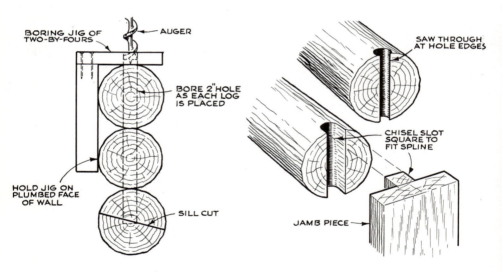

Fig. 11. Window opening framed by fitting jambs into slots in logs.

A better though more difficult construction suggested by the aforementioned Forest Service bulletin is shown in Fig. 11. Notch the bottom log of the opening after boring 2″ holes just outside the desired opening. Bore similar holes in each succeeding log, taking care to align them all. A boring jig like that shown might be improvised for this, but it will be effective only if the inner log edges are carefully aligned and plumb. Spike the logs together as you lay them. When the last full one at the top of the opening is in position, mark out the opening and saw through along the inside edges of the holes.

Square up the groove so formed with a chisel to fit a 2-by-2 spline nailed to the jamb piece. These splines will permit the logs to settle (as they must) yet hold them in alignment.

Whatever framing method is used, notch the header log deeply enough to allow for the top jamb piece, plus a settling allowance of 2″ for windows, about 3″ for doors. When the frame is in position and the header log set in place, fill the settling gap with compressible material such as rockwool insulation or crumpled building paper (Fig. 12). A sheetmetal drip cap placed as shown will keep water and wind out. As the roof load causes gradual settling of the upper wall logs, this header gap will prevent undue pressure on the door or window.

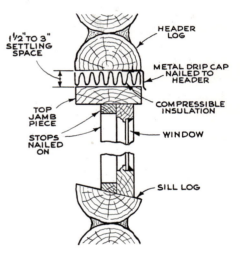

Fig. 12. Fully installed window with space left between top jamb and header log to allow for settling.

THE LOG CABIN ROOF. The familiar gable roof resembling an inverted V sheds rain well and will not accumulate an excessive load of snow. The plates, or top logs in the long side walls, support the rafters that frame the roof. These may be notched at an angle to rest on the flat-hewed tops of the plates as at A in Fig. 13., or the plate log may be notched instead to a snug fit for the rafters as at B. Either poles 4″ to 6″ in diameter, or sawed 2-by-4s, may be used for rafters in a small cabin. If logs are used for both plates and rafters, both may be notched as at C, Fig. 13. Still another method is shown at D.

The upper rafter ends meet at the ridgepole, a 2-by-6 (a true pole or log may be used, but the rafters should then be notched in). The important angle cut at the ridge end of the rafter, and the notch where it seats on the plate, are laid out with a steel framing square as explained in Chapter 8. In figuring the length, remember to add any desired eaves overhang.

Cut the ridge piece the same length as the plates. Erect the four end

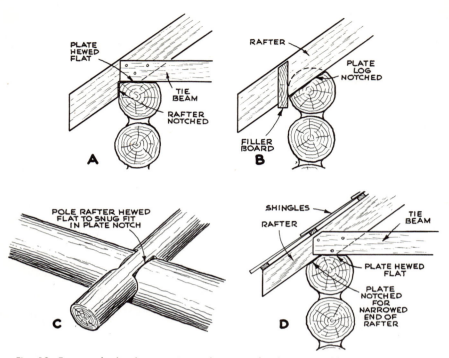

Fig. 13. Four methods of supporting rafters on top plates in gable-roof construction.

rafters first, toenailing them to the plates. Then place the intermediate rafters at 16″ center-to-center spacing.

As the weight of the roof tends to push the walls apart, the lower rafter ends should be held together with tie beams—2-by-4s, 2-by-6s, or 6″ poles. Nail these to the rafters where they cross the plates. These beams can be left exposed, or a wooden or panelboard ceiling laid over or under them. With the ceiling on top of 2-by-6 beams, and a ladder and guardrail fitted, the attic space so formed can be used for storage or extra bunk space for young-sters.

Hip roofs, which have four angled sides and resemble pyramids, are more difficult to frame. However, the angle cuts for these and roof valleys (where two gable roofs meet) can also be figured with the carpenter's steel square.

Covering the Roof. Whether you use shingles, the larger, thicker slabs known as shakes, or composition roofing, supporting pieces must be first nailed to the rafters. Log purlins—logs laid across the rafters at 2′ spacing for shakes, or closer for shingles—are sometimes used for log structures.

Four walls leave a big triangular opening under each end of a gable roof. Some builders close these by laying the end-wall logs all the way up, using successively shorter logs with the ends cut to the roof angle. Another method is to nail vertical boards to the end tie beam and end rafter, covering the joints between the boards with battens of ½″ or ¾″ lumber about 3″ wide. (Fig. 14). Logs or poles can be similarly used and made weathertight by chinking and calking.

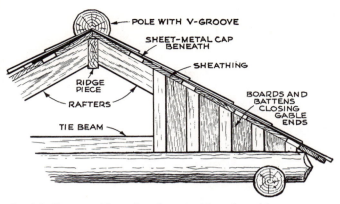

Fig. 14. Closing gable ends with vertical boards and battens.

Alternatively, plain boarding can be made watertight by covering it with small shingles, which blend well with log construction. A louvered ventilator, set into the gable end so that the louvers slant downward on the outside, helps dispel summer humidity and dampness. It should have a screen to keep out insects, and a hinged inside cover that can be closed in cold weather.

CHINKING AND CALKING. If logs have been well selected and carefully fitted, the gaps between them will be small and can be filled with calking compound. A calking gun makes this chore easier than a trowel, forcing the material well inside. Good calking compound remains flexible instead of hardening, and therefore does not pop out readily because of shrinkage and settling. It's best to do calking in mild weather; if it's cold, warm the compound gently.

Since any log cabin will be settling for a time, some calking will eventually be loosened or forced out. For this reason calking may profitably be delayed for some months if possible, to let the logs settle themselves first.

Where rough or irregular logs have been used, some gaps may be too large to hold calking. This calls for chinking—closing such openings at least in part with split wood, small poles, metal lath (a type of screening) or soft material such as oakum, the rock wool used for insulation batts, sphagnum moss or cotton waste. Small poles, however, are prone to split or loosen as they season. Soft packing should be driven in with a mallet and a calking tool made by grinding square the end of an old, wide chisel.

Figure 15 shows how chinking may be done. Don't forget to plug gaps between the walls and chimney, under the eaves, at floor edges and in gable ends to keep out weather, birds, small animals, and insects.

Field branches of the U.S. Forest Service recommend stapling strips of metal lath on the outside of cracks and filling in with chimney mortar. This should be mixed in small batches as it hardens quickly. Use two parts Portland cement, one of dry hydrated lime, and six of clean, screened sand with enough water to make a stiff paste.

The Oklahoma State University of Agriculture and Applied Science re-

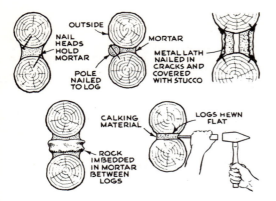

Fig. 15. Various methods of chinking the gaps between logs.

ports favorably on a method of chinking that bonds tenaciously to the logs, is elastic enough to cling even after logs shrink, and is not subject to insect or rodent attack. Spar varnish is first applied to the surfaces around gaps. While it is still tacky, brown or white rock wool is tamped in place with the end of a ⅜"-thick board. Either varnish or linseed oil is then brushed rapidly over the surface so that it does not penetrate deeply. If any of this chinking breaks loose, it need only be tamped back into place.

EXTERIOR FINISHES FOR LOG CABINS. Logs with the bark on should require only treatment with preservative from time to time, as already stated. Peeled logs can be left to weather naturally. Finishes have almost no effect on decay, but may help prevent insect infestation. Peeled logs will gradually darken of themselves, but, if you prefer, a stain with preservative added may be applied to darken them. Logwood oil, colorless or with burnt umber or raw sienna added, is sometimes used. Try any stain on an inconspicuous part first to make sure it will give the desired effect.

Stain is much easier to apply than paint, soaks in rapidly, doesn't crack or otherwise deteriorate, and lasts five years or more. Some modern stains, with less pigment than older, opaque ones, let wood grain show pleasingly but are somewhat shorter-lived.

Transparent linseed-oil, varnish and wood-seal finishes may need much more frequent renewal, especially if the cabin is fully exposed to the sun. Oil and wood seal are superior to varnish in that they won't alligator, crack or peel, and need not be removed when refinishing is necessary. A natural finish developed by the Forest Products Laboratory requires only a single coat and lasts three years or more.

Attractive effects are sometimes achieved by painting only the ends of the logs. The resulting modest color accent is in pleasing contrast to the more staid tone of the log walls.

OTHER KINDS OF LOG CONSTRUCTION. Plain tenon and dovetail corners are also used. Chinkless construction, popular in Scandinavian countries, requires grooving of all logs their full length. The upright groove-and-tenon corner is easier to make and mechanically advantageous, but also demands painstaking work.

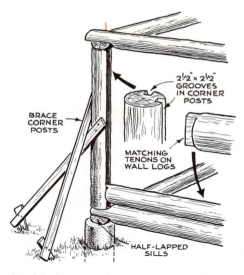

Fig. 16. Groove-and-tenon method of log-wall construction.

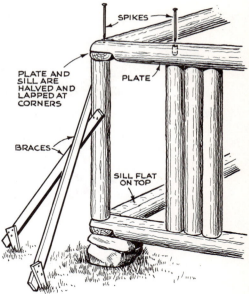

Fig. 17. Palisade log walls set vertically between flattened sill and plate logs.

For this, the sills are best half-lapped at the corners and all laid level at the same height (Fig. 16). Heavy corner logs are hewed flat on two sides 90 degrees apart, then grooved the full length of both these faces to receive 2½″ tenons cut on the ends of the horizontal logs. Alternatively, logs can be notched and splines fitted to them and the posts. The corner posts are pinned to the sills, extra grooved posts being used to frame door openings.

The construction of palisade walls with vertical logs is shown in Fig. 17. Sills should be hewn flat on top to a width equal to or slightly greater than the diameter of the uprights. The sill corners are lapped and sturdy corner logs pinned or spiked to them by toenailing. Brace these corner uprights with boards temporarily nailed to them and the sills as shown, plumbing them carefully from two directions. Lift the plate logs to the tops of the corner posts and spike them in place. Two or three 2″ planks can be used if you wish to avoid the labor of hewing logs flat on the underside. See that the plates are level.

Poles or logs 4″ in diameter and larger, with as little taper as possible, are now fitted between plates and sills. Hew each log flat on two opposite sides so that it butts neatly against the next. It's best to place these vertical logs upside down instead of the way they grew, so that water will drain out of knots and branch stubs. Cut each to fit snugly between plate and sill. Toenail it to the sill, preferably where the next post will cover the nail. At the top, drive spikes straight down through the plate into each log. It's a good idea to apply preservative to the sills and to both post ends.

For door and window openings, carefully plumb the last pole, allow enough space for the desired opening, and start setting poles on the other side.

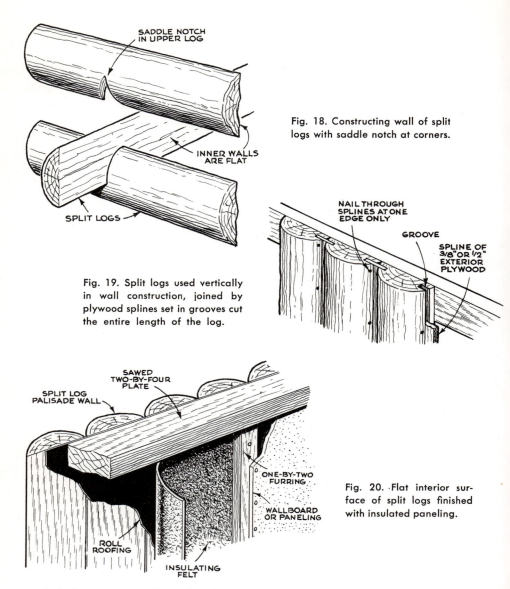

Fig. 18. Constructing wall of split logs with saddle notch at corners.

Fig. 19. Split logs used vertically in wall construction, joined by plywood splines set in grooves cut the entire length of the log.

Fig. 20. Flat interior surface of split logs finished with insulated paneling.

Split logs set on end are fine for outside walls as well as for interior partitions, but splitting them is a job for a sawmill. Walls of horizontal split logs can be erected by notching them as shown in Fig. 18. The saddle notch is always cut in the top log and slips over the one below it.

Log sections can also be grooved along the edges for splines of waterproof exterior plywood (Fig. 19). Each of these should be nailed in one section only. Floating free in the other, they will keep out water even if log sections shrink away from each other. Such split-log palisade walls afford a flat inside surface which may be finished with wallboard or paneling. Fig. 20 shows how roll roofing, insulating felt and dead air space created by furring strips underneath the paneling make a snug, weathertight wall.

CHAPTER EIGHT

FRAME, PANEL
AND OTHER STRUCTURES

THE SKELETON or framing of a house can be built in several ways. The method to be used is shown in most house plans, and may depend on the size of the structure, whether it has one story or two, and the kind of exterior wall siding to be used. But superseding all these considerations is the building code that may apply.

In some areas codes exert little control over structural details. In others they dictate minimum requirements for everything from the number and spacing of foundation piers to the type of roof covering. You may have to submit a drawing of the proposed structure to get a local building permit. Even with this in hand, it is still up to you to study applicable ordinances and make sure the work will meet all code requirements.

Since these do vary, it should be understood that the following can be only general recommendations, although based on good practice and data from the National Lumber Manufacturers Association and other authorities.

BUILDING ON FOUNDATION WALLS. With continuous foundation walls, the underpinning or floor support (on which the entire house will stand) usually consists of 2-by-6 or 2-by-8 sills laid flat. It's desirable that sills be of naturally decay-resistant woods like cypress or redwood, or else creosoted or otherwise treated to resist decay and termite infestation.

Place sills in their intended positions, pushing them against the anchor bolts set into the foundation and carefully lining up their ends. With a try square, mark the position of each bolt on the sill. Then cross-mark each hole location, taking account of the distance the bolt is set in from the face of the foundation wall, and whether sheathing is to be flush with this wall or not.

At corners, one sill should be fastened down with an anchor bolt; the other is simply butted against the first and toenailed to it. If long, this sill too should be tied down with at least two anchor bolts no more than 8' apart.

Bore the bolt holes in the sills about $\frac{1}{16}''$ larger than the bolts. Mix equal amounts of sand and cement with water to make a grout the consistency of thin paste. Thoroughly wet the top of the foundation wall. Apply a generous layer of grout to it, and set the sills on their anchor bolts and into the grout.

Check each sill with a long level. Hammer down the high end if necessary. Toenail butted sills with 8d nails. Put a washer on each bolt and draw up the nut, but not so tightly as to tilt the sill off the level. Check frequently; sills should not only be level, but of the same height all around. Time spent to get the sill bed true will spare you the trouble of correcting for deviations later.

POST AND PIER UNDERPINNING. Concrete piers may be used to support the entire structure, to support partitions or interior walls between full foundation walls, or to support a span that otherwise would be excessive for floor joists. For hillside houses, piers and posts are necessary to compensate for the slope of the ground.

When piers are used to support the entire structure, 4-by-6 sills are laid, on which the floor joists will later rest. The sills, in order to carry the load between piers, are set on edge (Fig. 1) and tied down securely with anchor bolts embedded in the piers.

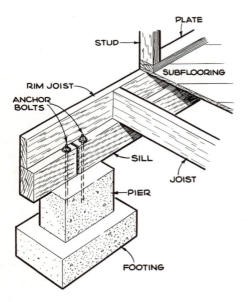

Fig. 1. Pier foundation with 4-by-6 sill laid on edge and tied down with bolts embedded in concrete.

If piers are to be used to support partitions or interior walls between full foundation walls, 4-by-4 posts are erected on each pier to bring the supporting base up to the level of the foundation walls. (Posts may be necessary in simple pier foundations if the piers are not the suggested 18″ high.) On these posts the girders, either heavy timbers or built-up beams of smaller stock, are laid parallel with the foundation walls to support the floor joists.

To prevent lateral movement of the posts, especially in areas subject to earthquake, a steel pin is embedded in each pier when it is cast. The post is bored to fit over the pin. Another method, acceptable where quakes are uncommon, is to set a pier block on top of the pier. The block is a piece of 2″ stock 6″ or 8″ square, laid in grout. Wet the top of the pier, apply grout, press the block into it, and level it in both directions by tapping down the high sides.

When the grout has set, the 4-by-4 post is toenailed to the pier block with at least four 8d nails. Each post must be individually cut to correct length so that the top of all posts will provide a level support for the girder that rests on them. To measure post lengths, stretch a line taut across two points indicating the required girder height (Fig. 2). Add ¼″ to the distance from the pier or pier block to the line (to compensate for line sag). Then deduct the actual width (in effect the height) of the girder.

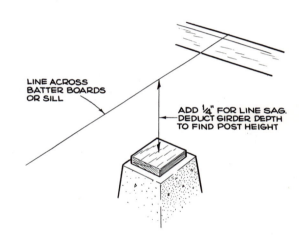

LINE ACROSS
BATTER BOARDS
OR SILL

ADD ¼″ FOR LINE SAG.
DEDUCT GIRDER DEPTH
TO FIND POST HEIGHT

Fig. 2. Line stretched between sills or batter boards to find post height when using posts and piers to support partition walls.

Built-up Beams and Girders. When heavy timbers aren't available, or command a premium price, you can build up beams and girders by nailing together lengths of 2″ stock. Use 16d nails, driving them in two rows along the top and bottom edges and about 32″ apart. Carriage bolts spaced 24″ apart, with washers under the nuts, are even better. Built-up girders are preferably installed with the faces of their component members vertical, for best load resistance (Fig. 3).

PLATFORM AND BALLOON FRAMING. The popularity of these two methods varies in different parts of the country. In platform frame construction (Fig. 4), floor joists are laid on the sills and a subfloor of diagonal boards is nailed on top of the joists. Then 2-by-4 sole plates are nailed around the edges of the floor in a flat position. The vertical studs—2-by-4s that form the walls and support the second floor and roof—are set on the sole plates. Similar top plates, usually doubled, are nailed across the upper ends of the studs. If there is to be a second floor, joists are laid on these plates, a second sub-

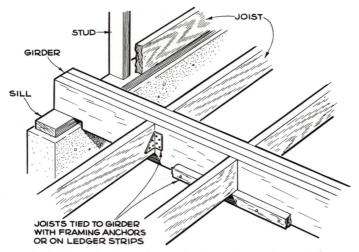

Fig. 3. Girder built up of 2-by-6s. Two methods are shown of tying joists to girder.

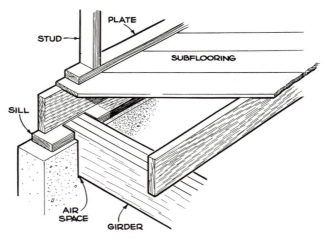

Fig. 4. Platform frame construction.

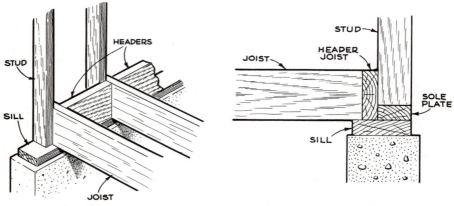

Fig. 5. Balloon construction.

Fig. 6. T-sill construction.

floor nailed down, and the second-story studs erected on a second tier of sole plates.

In balloon frame construction, the studs and joists both rest directly on the sills (Fig. 5). The subfloor must be notched around the studs. In a two-story house the studs run the full height of both stories, and the second-floor joists rest on a 1-by-4 "ribbon strip" let into notches in the studs.

There are still other kinds of sill construction. In the T sill, for example, the studs rest on a sole plate laid directly on the sill; joists are connected inside the studs by a continuous header or cross joist (Fig. 6).

In platform frame construction, pockets are sometimes formed in foundation walls for the ends of girders, sinking them to the level of the sills (Fig. 4). There should be ½" of air space at the ends and sides of the girders to avoid subjecting them to excessive moisture, unless they are of durable or treated wood.

When foundation pockets are not practical, and in balloon frame construction, girders are set on the sill but notched at the bottom, if necessary, to bring their top surface level with that of the joists (Fig. 3). At least 4" of the end of a girder should bear on its support. Joints in girders should be avoided if possible; if used, they should be over a supporting post (Fig. 7).

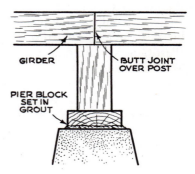

Fig. 7. Girder joined over 4-by-4 post set on concrete pier.

GIRDER

BUTT JOINT OVER POST

PIER BLOCK SET IN GROUT

LAYING THE FLOOR JOISTS. These form a level framework over which the subfloor is laid. Codes usually specify lumber sizes for joists of various lengths. In general, 2-by-6s may be used up to 10'. For 12' spans, use 2-by-8s; for 16', 2-by-10s. A girder midway of the span cuts it in half and permits the use of lighter joists. However, joists should in all cases be sound, free of loose or large edge knots, and of a size conforming to code requirements. Standard joist spacing is 16", but 24" spacing is sometimes used. At least 1½" of the joist's end should bear on its support.

Joists are usually laid the short way of the area to be spanned, for obvious reasons. Start by marking joist locations off along the longest wall. A straight 1-by-3 may profitably be marked as a layout template. With the steel square, set off desired joist intervals from one end (measuring from one face of a joist to the corresponding face of the next, if they are of uniform thickness, is the same as center-to-center spacing). Mark the joist thickness at the end

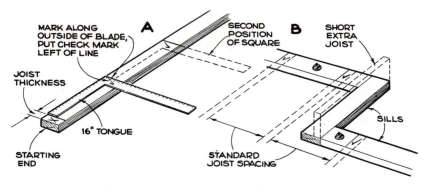

Fig. 8. Laying out joist spacing along sill with framing square.

of the template as the starting point, measure 16″ (or 24″) from this, square a line across, and put a check mark inside it (Fig. 8A).

Place the template against the sill, its end flush with the sill's, and transfer the lines and check marks to the sill. The checks show on which side of the lines the joists shall go; when in position, they will cover the checks. In marking the opposite sill, be sure you start at the same end and with the template's starting end flush with the sill's; the template must not be reversed. At offsets or jogs, add a short joist but space the next full one exactly 16″ or 24″ from the previous long one (Fig. 8B).

Joists should be doubled under partition walls running parallel to them, because the load carried by such a wall will rest on the doubled joists alone. (Partitions at right angles to joists are amply supported by several of them.) To double joists, either spike them solidly together or insert blocking to leave a space between for wiring or pipes that are to run through the wall. In other joists, holes for wiring or pipes should not be nearer than 2″ to either edge, nor larger than one third the joist's depth. Notches for such purposes should be no more than one sixth the depth, and should not be located in the middle third of the joist's length.

When the top of the girder is at joist level, the joists must be supported on ledger strips nailed along the bottom of the girder as in Fig. 3, or with metal framing anchors or saddles as shown. If the girder is at sill height, joists simply rest on top of it. They should be cut long enough to overlap about 12″, and nailed to each other as well as to the girder (Fig. 9).

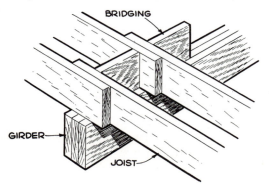

Fig. 9. Joists resting on top of girder are overlapped, braced with solid bridging.

To keep the floor load from tilting joists off the vertical, either header joists (rim joists) are spiked across their ends, or short headers of the same stock are cut to fit snugly between each pair of joists as in Fig. 5. The continuous header, sometimes called a rim joist, takes up sill space and so leaves less for the joists to bear on. Headers set between joists leave about 2″ more of bearing space on the sill. Some codes require these.

If rim joists are to be used, nail these first to the two end joists with 16d nails. Toenail rim joists to the sills with 8d common nails about 24″ apart. Cut all other joists carefully to length; if too long, they may force the wall out of line. Fasten them by driving two 16d nails through the rim joist into each cross joist. In addition, toenail each joist to the sills or girders it rests on with two 8d nails.

If separate headers are to be used, see that joists are cut to come flush with the outer edges of the sills. In all cases, sight along each joist to determine whether it has a crown or curve toward one edge. If so, place it with the convex edge upward. However, badly warped joists should not be used. Check laid joists frequently with a straightedge; they should form an even, level surface for the floor.

Framing Floor and Ceiling Openings. A conventional fireplace hearth, inside chimney, or stairway requires a hole in the floor or ceiling, and this opening must be framed within the joists. Fireplace framing is shown in Fig. 10. However, there are prefabricated fireplace units that permit installation where no such provision has been made for a concrete hearth slab.

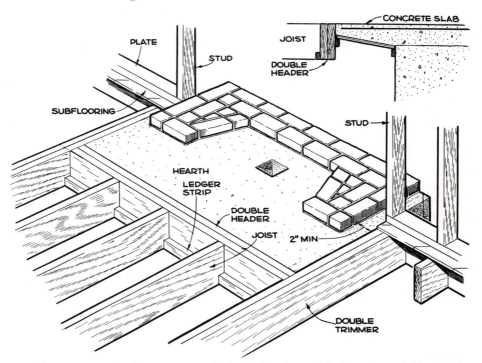

Fig. 10. Framing a fireplace opening with double header and double trimmer joists. Detail at top shows how concrete slab is poured.

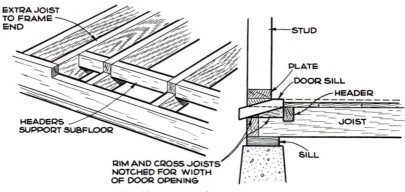

EXTRA JOIST
TO FRAME
END

STUD

PLATE

DOOR SILL

HEADER

JOIST

HEADERS
SUPPORT SUBFLOOR

SILL

RIM AND CROSS JOISTS
NOTCHED FOR WIDTH
OF DOOR OPENING

Fig. 11. Framing door openings.

A special kind of opening must be provided in floor joists at door sills. The header and joists are notched to accommodate the door sill; then small headers are fitted between the joists, back of the notches, to support the subfloor (Fig. 11).

Bridging Stiffens Joists. If joists are free to move slightly from their vertical position, the result is a squeaky and perhaps saggy floor. Joists longer than 8' should have bridging midway of their length, long joists every 8'.

Two kinds of bridging are common. Solid bridging (Fig. 12) must be cut accurately and squarely to length. It is much easier to install if staggered instead of placed in a straight line. Two 16d nails can thus be driven through each joist into one end of a piece of bridging. Be sure that the top edges of solid bridging are flush with the joists.

Diagonal or herringbone bridging (Fig. 13) requires angle cuts, and the bottom ends should be nailed fast only after the subfloor is down—an awkward job where crawl space is tight. The angle cuts can be laid out with a framing square as shown in Fig. 14. Measure between several joists to determine the average horizontal distance, or run, between them. Also measure the actual joist height, or rise.

Hold the square on the *edge* of the bridging stock with the rise figure on the tongue exactly at the nearer arris, or corner, of the stock, and the run figure on the blade at the far arris. Now draw a line outside the tongue, and put a mark at the run figure.

Shift the square to the right until the outside of the tongue touches this mark, with the rise figure as before on the lower arris and the run figure on the upper. Draw a line along the tongue again and you have marked one piece of bridging. Mark the run figure again, move the square once more, and so on. Remember to align rise and run figures on *opposite* corners of the stock; this automatically compensates for stock thickness.

Start two 8d nails into each end of a piece at right angles to the cut. Run a line across the joists where the bridging is to go. Between each pair of joists place one piece on one side of the line, one on the other, so forming an "X". Nail the upper ends fast, taking care that no bridging protrudes above the joists. After the subfloor is down, push the lower ends firmly into place and nail them. Having the nails started makes this much easier. (The subfloor

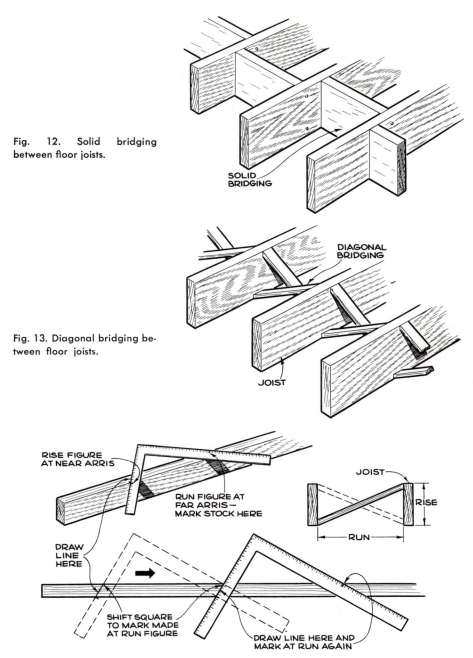

Fig. 12. Solid bridging between floor joists.

SOLID BRIDGING

DIAGONAL BRIDGING

Fig. 13. Diagonal bridging between floor joists.

JOIST

RISE FIGURE AT NEAR ARRIS

RUN FIGURE AT FAR ARRIS— MARK STOCK HERE

JOIST

RISE

RUN

DRAW LINE HERE

SHIFT SQUARE TO MARK MADE AT RUN FIGURE

DRAW LINE HERE AND MARK AT RUN AGAIN

Fig. 14. Laying out diagonal bridging with the framing square.

tends to pull any slight unevenness in the joists into line, but the bridging would resist this if prematurely nailed.)

Metal bridging is available. It saves the time and labor required to make angle cuts, but costs more for material, whereas scrap can be used for wooden bridging.

LAYING THE SUBFLOOR. Conventional subflooring is 1-by-6 stock, either square-edged or tongue-and-groove. It is usually laid at an angle of 45 degrees to the joists, because finish flooring may then be laid either crosswise or parallel to the joists.

Mark equal distances (8′ to 10′) from one corner. Lay a flooring board across the two marks, and nail it to each joist it crosses with two 8d box nails driven about ¾″ inside the edges of the board. In laying subsequent boards, see that the outer edge lies parallel to the previous board. Check by measuring occasionally both ways from the corner. Where joints must be made, cut the ends of both boards at 45 degrees to center the joint squarely over a joist, and nail both ends of both boards. (End-matched lumber in long lengths, with factory-made joints, is available at extra cost.) Stagger joints to avoid having two side by side on the same joist.

When all the boards are down, saw them flush with the outer faces of the perimeter joists. This is much speedier than cutting boards to length individually.

Plywood is often used for the subfloor. It is uniform in thickness, the large panels hold joints to a minimum, and they go down more quickly. Some codes permit wider joist spacing under plywood subflooring. The ⅝″ thickness is commonly used, but several others are available, an important consideration in matching the level of different kinds of flooring such as hardwood, linoleum, carpeting and tile. Often plywood is used for concrete foundation forms, then cleaned up and used for subflooring or wall sheathing.

The face grain of plywood subflooring is laid at right angles to the joists. Blocking must be nailed between joists under the joint line of adjacent panels. Plywood subflooring is fastened with 8d common nails 6″ apart along panel edges, 10″ apart inside. If tile, linoleum or other resilient floor coverings are to be laid (instead of a wood finish floor), a second layer of thin plywood or hardboard, called underlayment, is required. However, there is a seven-ply, 1⅛″ thick panel that can be laid as a combination subfloor and underlayment. This "2-4-1" grade is available with either straight or tongue-and-groove edges. With the latter, it requires no blocking, and where codes permit the floor beams may be 48″ apart.

ASSEMBLING THE WALLS. Vertical 2-by-4 studs form the framework of the walls. They carry the entire load of the superstructure. Studs are all placed with their faces—the nominal 4″ dimension—at right angles to the wall line, except when studs are grouped to form corner posts.

In balloon framing, since studs and joists both rest on the sills, they are facenailed together and toenailed to the sills. In platform frame construction, 2-by-4 bottom or sole plates are nailed to the subfloor and the studs stand on these. Check room measurements carefully against the plans and align the plates on the subfloor accordingly. Facenail them with 16d nails driven into the joists.

Next, saw all the studs to the length specified in the plans. A simple frame temporarily nailed to the subfloor will hold a number of pieces in alignment

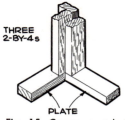

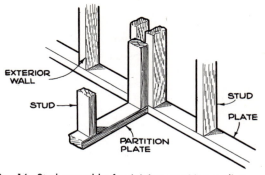

Fig. 15. Corner post built up of three 2-by-4s.

Fig. 16. Stud assembly for joining partition wall to exterior wall, to provide interior nailing flanges.

so that they can be cut simultaneously. It is also possible to buy studs precut to standard lengths.

Corner posts are built up of three studs, less for extra strength than to provide nailing flanges for interior wall material. There are several ways to build up corner posts. One of the best is shown in Fig. 15. The three pieces, selected for straightness, are nailed together with 16d nails 24″ apart. Where partition walls are to start from an exterior wall, three studs are assembled as in Fig. 16. The right-angled one rests on the sole plate of the partition.

Lay out stud positions on the sole plates, starting from one side or one end of the building. Though standard stud spacing is 16″, studs are often 24″ apart in one-story structures. Measure 48″ from the inside corner formed by the corner-post members, mark this point, and draw a line 1″ each side of it to represent the faces of a stud. With the steel square, lay out other stud locations from this one in both directions.

Cut top plates to the same lengths as sole plates or, if a joint is required, size top-plate sections to bring the joint directly over a stud. Place a top plate against the sole plate to transfer stud markings.

Instead of erecting studs separately on the sole plate, it's common practice to join studs with the top plate and then raise them into position on the sole plate. Another method is to build wall sections consisting of sole plate, studs and top plate. One advantage of this is that you can drive nails through the sole plate into the ends of the studs instead of toenailing these. Such a frame is raised and the sole plate then spiked to the joists.

Wall sections are best assembled flat on the subfloor. Assuming that the plates are nailed down, you can butt the studs against the sole plate on which they will eventually stand, aligning them with the marks made on sole and top plate, and drive two 16d nails through the top plate into each stud. Do not use badly bowed or warped studs if you can avoid doing so, but if some are slightly crowned, place them with the bellied edges alternately up and down so that they will tend to cancel each other out. Tack light braces from the corner posts across several end studs to the top plate to hold the section in shape.

RAISING THE WALLS. The assembly can be braced against the fixed sole plate while it is being raised. Lift it atop the sole plate and plumb the corner

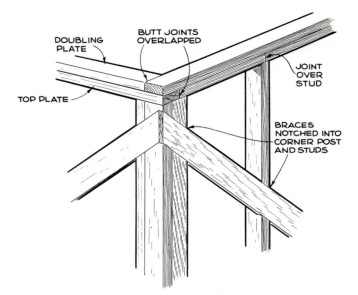

DOUBLING PLATE

BUTT JOINTS OVERLAPPED

JOINT OVER STUD

TOP PLATE

BRACES NOTCHED INTO CORNER POST AND STUDS

Fig. 17. Butt joints of doubling plate overlap those of top plates.

posts in both directions. A helper should stand ready to nail diagonal braces from each corner post to the sole plate, and a cross brace or two from an internal stud to a partition plate or the subfloor. The next wall, when erected, will further brace the first. Toenail each stud and corner post to the sole plate with two 8d nails.

A second 2-by-4, called a doubling plate, is nailed on top of the top plate after the wall is raised. It requires no stud markings, but should be cut to a length to overlap top-plate joints at the corner posts (Fig. 17). Any joints in the doubling plate should be away from those in the top plate.

Some builders use continuous headers instead of top plates. These headers are two pieces of 2″ stock set on edge. Joints in one of these should be at least three stud spaces from any joint in the other, and never over door or window openings. Headers are toenailed to the studs and corner posts. Corner joints should overlap as shown in Fig. 18, and can be reinforced with metal caps or straps.

Permanent wall bracing is necessary if the outer wall is to be of horizontal or composition sheathing, which adds little lateral strength. Braces are usually of 1-by-4 stock let into the studs, each of which must be notched to the correct width and angle. Braces should run from the tops of corner posts to the bottoms of sole plates at the third or fourth stud.

Another kind of brace consists of short pieces of 2-by-4 fitted between the studs in a straight line. To mark the pieces for cutting, tack-nail a light strip outside the studs from post to bottom plate at the angle the brace will be placed. Lay the 2-by-4 on this strip, flat, with one edge touching the studs. Draw lines on this edge along the faces of two adjacent studs. Slide the stock to bring one line inside the next stud interval and mark that. Cut the two end pieces to abutt both stud (or corner post) and plate, as shown in Fig. 19. Square the lines across the face and saw the pieces apart. Start two 8d nails

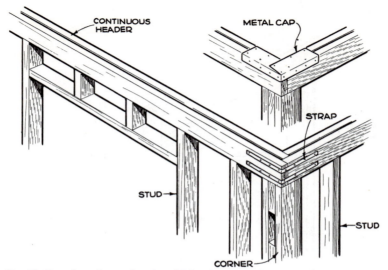

Fig. 18. Use of continuous header of 2-by-4s set on edge, instead of doubling plate. Two ways of handling corners are shown.

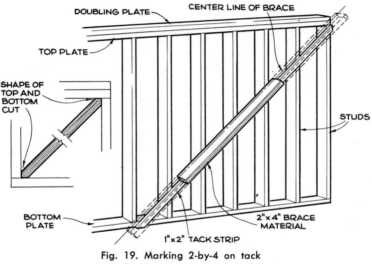

Fig. 19. Marking 2-by-4 on tack strip for braces set between studs.

into each end at right angles to the cut, but set all pieces in position before nailing any tight. If diagonal or plywood wall sheathing is used, bracing may not be necessary.

FRAMING WALL OPENINGS. Any door or window opening would weaken the wall if the gap were not solidly framed with extra members. Since such openings may not coincide with regular stud spacing (which must be maintained to fit interior wall materials), extra studs, called opening studs, must be fitted. The spacing of these must take into account the thickness of trimmers, jamb stock, sashweight pockets if required, and the width of the

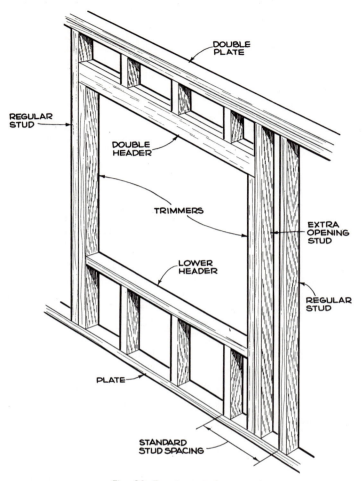

Fig. 20. Framing window openings.

door or window sash. (It is of course sometimes possible to use a regular stud as an opening stud.)

Trimmers are shorter pieces of studding facenailed inside the opening studs (Fig. 20). Trimmers also rest on the sole plate, so doubling the vertical support for the header, which spans the top of the opening. This top header, usually two pieces of stock set on edge for maximum stiffness, rests directly on the trimmers. The bottom header, across the bottom of a window opening, is studding laid flat between the trimmers. Short studs at standard spacing from the regular studs are fitted between the top plate and top header, and between sole plate and bottom header.

Some builders erect wall sections with full studs all around, and cut out openings for doors and windows later. This saves time, and the pieces cut out can usually be put to good use. Other builders set in opening studs, top headers and the short studs above them on the ground, leaving trimmers and bottom headers out until the wall is raised.

THE CEILING JOISTS. Apart from providing a framework for a flat ceiling, ceiling joists tie together the side walls and, by keeping the rafters from spreading, help the roof resist snow loads. The U.S. Forest Service recommends 2-by-6 joists spaced 16″ center to center for cabins in snowy regions. Where heavy roof loads are not likely and the joist span small, 2-by-4s are often used.

To perform their function, ceiling joists should be placed crosswise of the side walls (that is, parallel to the gable or end walls). If the span is too long for a single joist, a lap joint should be made over a partition wall (Fig. 21).

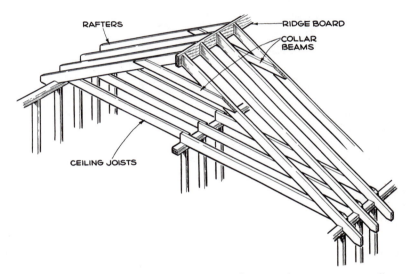

Fig. 21. Framing roof and ceiling. Ceiling joists lap-jointed over partition wall.

FRAMING THE ROOF. This is the most difficult part of house framing, particularly if the plans specify a hip roof or one with intersecting parts, rather than the simpler shed or gable roof. Then it is advisable to get expert assistance in laying out and determining the various angle cuts necessary for such a roof.

The geometry of a common gable roof is shown in Fig. 22. The *span* is the distance across the outer edges of the top plates on opposite walls. The *run* is one half of this, from one plate to the vertical ridge line. The height of the ridge point above the plates is the *rise*. The proportion of rise to span is called the *pitch* of the roof, expressed as a fraction. A roof of 30′ span with a 10′ rise has a pitch of ⅓. One of 24′ span with a 6′ rise is of ¼ pitch.

As the rise, run and rafter slope of each half of a gable roof form a right-angled triangle, we can use the steel square to lay out rafter angles and determine rafter length. To do so, we must use 12″ as the unit of run. To find the inches of rise per 12″ of run, we multiply the unit of span (twice the run,

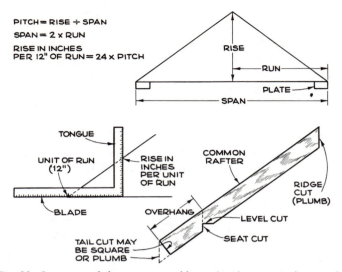

Fig. 22. Geometry of the common gable roof with its equivalent on the framing square. Also shown are the three cuts made on each rafter.

or 24) by the pitch. (Since the pitch is a fraction, this means dividing by its denominator.) Therefore a pitch of ⅓ has 8″ of rise per 12″ of run; a pitch of ½ would have 12″, and a roof of ⅙ pitch 4″ rise per foot.

Carpenters call the rise in inches per 12″ of run the *cut* of the roof. A ⅙ pitch roof has a cut of 4 and 12, a ⅓ pitch roof has an 8 and 12 cut.

Figure 22 shows how the framing square duplicates in miniature the exact rafter angle of the full-size roof. For laying out a master rafter, clamp a straight piece of light wood across the square, aligning it at the figure 12 on the 24″ blade and at the rise figure on the 16″ tongue. Both figures are those on the outer edges of the square. With the wood strip affixed, the square can be slid along the rafter stock and will maintain the same angular setting at all positions. Level cuts will be marked along the blade or run dimension. All plumb or vertical cuts will be drawn along the tongue or rise line. To lay out a master rafter, use the square as follows (Fig. 23).

1. From one end of the stock, measure the distance rafters will overhang the top plate. Mark the stock.

2. With the wood strip on the square, slide it to align the rise figure on the tongue with this overhang mark.

3. Draw a line along the outer edge of the tongue.

4. Mark the desired depth of the seat cut (usually half the rafter width or less) on this line.

5. Slide the square to the right until the lower edge of the blade is at this last mark.

6. Draw a line along outer edge of blade. This outlines the seat cut.

7. Slide the square to the right until the 12 is at the overhang mark.

8. Make a mark at the rise figure on the tongue. This represents rafter length for one foot of run. Repeat the last step, placing the 12 at the last mark made, and marking the stock at the rise figure, as many times as there are feet of run in the roof.

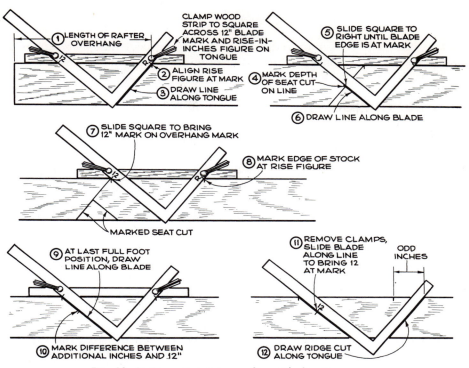

Fig. 23. Laying out common rafter with framing square.

9. To lay out a fractional foot, hold the square at the last full-foot position and draw a line along outer edge of the blade.

10. Deduct the additional inches from 12 and mark the line at the difference. (Example: if the run is 12′ 8″, mark off 12 times, draw the line, and make a mark at the figure 4 on the blade (12 minus 8).

11. Now remove the clamps from the square and slide the blade down along the drawn line until the 12 is at the mark on the line. Make sure the blade is on the line and parallel to it.

12. Draw a line along outer edge of the tongue. This is the ridge cut at the correct rafter length, for rafters that are to meet at the ridge point.

More often, there is a ridge piece between the rafters. To allow for this, rafters should be shorter by half the thickness of the ridge piece, measured at right angles to the ridge cut. If the run is a whole number in feet, you can draw a line along the blade at the last position, slide the blade *up* the line by this thickness allowance, and draw the ridge cut along the tongue. If the run includes a fractional foot, slide the blade down with the 12 short of the additional-inch mark by the thickness allowance.

Some framing squares have tables of rafter lengths engraved on them. Full information on these and on laying out hip, valley and jack rafters may be found in booklets that come with a framing square.

For a shed roof, the run is measured from the outside of the top plate on the lower wall to the inside of the top plate on the higher wall. Rafter layout is otherwise similar to that for a gable roof, except that there are two seat cuts instead of one, and the rafter often overhangs at the high end as well as the low.

RAISING THE ROOF. The ridge piece should be a straight piece of 2″ stock about 2″ wider than the rafters to offer them a full bearing surface. It may be the same length as the top plates or somewhat longer if used for a framed roof overhang at the gable ends. Lay out the location of every rafter on the ridge piece, squaring two lines for each across both sides. Mark identical rafter locations on the top plates; the rafters are placed alongside ceiling joists, and nailed to them.

Choose the straightest rafters for the gable ends. Toenail one to the ridge piece. With a helper holding the latter level, toenail the rafter to the plate with three 8d nails. Set in the opposite rafter. Nail two rafters in position at the other gable end, then brace the roof framing from the ridge piece to the top plate. Fill in with the other rafters at marked locations, facenailing them to the joists and toenailing them to the plates. In some areas where high winds or heavy snow impose severe loads, collar beams of 1-by-6 stock are nailed across every third pair of rafters.

For working safety, wide 2″ boards should be nailed across the ceiling joists under the ridge line. If the roof pitch is steep, it may be necessary to erect a simple scaffold of planks on a framework at each end, with braces to the ceiling joists.

At the gable ends, studs of varying length are usually framed between the top plates and the end rafters (Fig. 24) directly over wall studs. The upper ends are notched around the rafter. You can lay out the angle cut with the square, using the same run and rise figures as for the rafters. Mark the cut

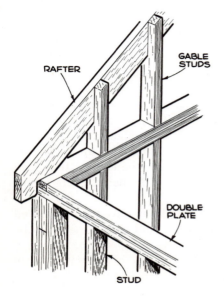

RAFTER

GABLE
STUDS

DOUBLE
PLATE

STUD

Fig. 24. Gable studs notched around rafter.

along the rise dimension. To find the difference in length for each stud, multiply the rise per foot by 1⅓ if studs are spaced 16″, by 2 if stud spacing is 24″. Gable studs must be carefully cut; if too long or too short, they may force the rafter out of alignment.

For roll or composition roofing, a sheathing of 1-by-6 boards should be nailed to the rafters to form a solid surface. For wood shingles, 1-by-4s may be spaced their width apart. Drive two 8d nails through each board into every rafter.

Plywood sheathing is also used to advantage. Some modern vacation-home plans include a panelized system of roof sheathing making use of precut plywood panels.

Roof framing may consist of prefabricated trusses instead of rafters and ceiling joists. Built to sound engineering standards, trusses can bridge extra-wide spans without partitions, posts or other supports under them, so creating large and unimpeded living areas. No ceiling joists are needed, for the lower chord or horizontal member of the truss is in effect a joist (Fig. 25).

Being triangular in form, trusses are self-supporting and easy to transport and erect, speeding on-site construction. Truss spacing is commonly 16″ or 24″. Solid lumber is usually used for the chords and braces, plywood for the gussets or plates that reinforce joints. Members may be glued, nailed, bolted or joined with patented connectors.

PANELIZED CONSTRUCTION. This ingenious and comparatively new building method splits big walls into modular or panel units, sized to accommodate modern materials. It reduces the amount of on-site labor necessary to build the shell of the house. Panel units can be fabricated in one's home garage, carport or basement in spare time, including winter months, and then trucked to the building site and erected comparatively quickly.

A good example of panelized construction is Masonite's No. AB-204-1. It calls for a slab foundation with two anchor bolts set in for each panel, and an extra chimney footing. Only five kinds of panels are used, all built up of

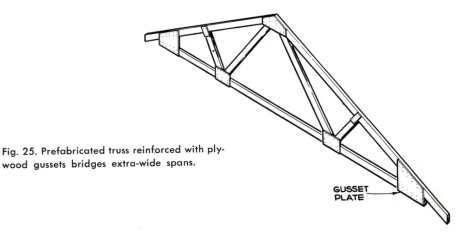

Fig. 25. Prefabricated truss reinforced with plywood gussets bridges extra-wide spans.

GUSSET
PLATE

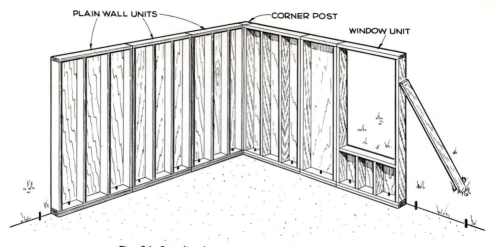

Fig. 26. Panelized construction on slab foundation.

2-by-4s, and one of each may be used as a jig for cutting stock and assembling the others. Basic wall panels consist of four studs 16″ apart between a sole plate and a top plate. Door and window panels have necessary openings framed within them. Except for three higher center panels that fit under the roof ridge, all are the same 4′-by-8′ size.

After the framing is nailed together, standard sheets of 5/16″ siding or 1/4″ hardboard are nailed on. This exterior siding material extends past the sole plate and top plate slightly. Each panel is then tipped up into place, bolted down, and nailed to the preceding panel unit (Fig. 26).

This system provides doubled studs between panels, making a sturdy wall. At corners, two extra 2-by-4s or a 4-by-4 post is set into adjacent panel edges. The siding material overhangs the edge of the slab and, with sill sealer under the sole plate, forms a watertight joint. When a full wall is up, a continuous doubling plate is nailed on top of the line of panels. Interior wall paneling is then applied inside.

A ridge beam and rafters frame the roof, the rafters being fastened to exterior-wall top plates with metal framing anchors. Although conventional sheathing and asphalt roofing can be used, an alternative is 1/4″ tempered hardboard applied without sheathing. Joints in this material are sealed by a non-hardening calking material and nailed battens. The roof is then finished with deck paint or a special roof coating.

THE A-FRAME VACATION HOME. Although A-frame structures go far back to antiquity, and were built long ago by Indians, trappers and hunters, they are as modern as tomorrow for leisure homes. Architects have rung some startling innovations on the basic theme, ranging from modest vacation shelters to ultrasmart second homes.

The A-frame has great structural advantages. Its triangular shape—actually a type of truss—is self-sustaining and the most rigid structural form known. It requires fewer parts than conventional framing. The floor area of the A-frame house is uncluttered by supporting posts. Its steep roof sheds snow, rain and ice even without the usual waterproof roof covering. The high peaked ceiling helps keep the living area cool.

For the do-it-yourself builder there are further bonuses. The A-frames are simple triangles, easily fabricated on the ground. As few as four or five frames may be enough for a fair-sized cottage. There are no difficult angle cuts, no top plates or studding, no complicated gable framing in the basic A-frame structure. A small house can readily be added to at any time by erecting more frames at either end. A second floor is easily provided by running beams across as the bar of the "A."

The most popular frame proportion seems to be that of an equilateral triangle; all three frame angles are 60 degrees, making the base and sides of equal length and simplifying the cutting of lumber. For extra headroom, the side angles are sometimes increased to 65 or 70 degrees. In high-wind areas, cross bracing with collar beams is recommended (the joists of a second floor would serve the same purpose).

The first carefully made frame can serve as a jig on which to build the others. Frames may be built with doubled floor joists and single rafters (Fig. 27A) or with single joists and doubled rafters (Fig. 27B). These members may be heavier than those used for conventional framing, although in small A-frame cabins rafters and joists may be as light as 2-by-6. More often

A-frame structure is extremely rigid, economical and easy to build. This cabin has an upper level for use as a sleeping loft. Cantilever deck serves as observation platform and boat-storage area. *Courtesy Potlatch Forests, Inc.*

rafters are 2-by-8s or 2-by-10s, joists 2-by-10s or 2-by-12s. They are either spiked or bolted together at the three corners, sometimes with gussets as well.

Erecting the Structure. Window and door openings can be built into the end frames on the ground. The piers and sills being down, frames are hoisted into position one at a time; as few as three people can erect the average-sized A-frame cottage. Frame spacing is usually 4'. The frames are temporarily braced while siding is applied.

Panel siding such as exterior plywood or tempered hardboard goes up more quickly and provides more longitudinal bracing than does horizontal siding. It is possible to work on the steep roof by standing on cleats temporarily nailed to the frames.

One disadvantage of the A-frame house is that doors built into the sloping side walls aren't practical—you literally have to lift a door to open it. If such

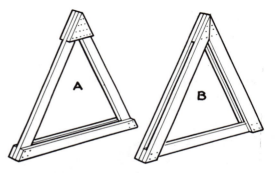

Fig. 27. Two types of A-frames.

an entrance is a "must," the only solution is a sort of dormer structure that will permit the door to be hung plumb. Windows built into the sloping sides can be pleasing, but require fussy sealing and drip caps at head and sill, for water tends to reverse its direction at these points and flow inside.

Headroom shrinks severely along the side walls. These areas are therefore best reserved for built-ins, storage, and bunk beds. Some designs strive to make better use of side-wall space by leaving part of the wall open (usually before a terrace or deck), or by extending a shed roof or dormer from it. Others show additional A-frames extending over a deck at the end of the building, with adjustable canvas panels that can be raised to admit sun or lowered for shade.

Like other vacation homes, A-frame units are available in prefabricated form. The buyer can put up the structure himself or have a contractor do so.

CHAPTER NINE

PORCHES AND OUTSIDE WALLS

ALTHOUGH A porch on a vacation home may seem merely a pleasant after-thought, it is a very important adjunct and often becomes the most popular part of the accommodations. In fair weather, hammocks, chairs, a card table and fresh air will lure the family to the porch for relaxation. Dining on the porch in the cool of the evening will be a delight, and if screens are installed, some may elect to sleep on the porch, which in effect becomes an extra room.

It is structurally soundest, and probably costs less, to incorporate a porch, in the original planning of your cabin. For a small porch at a gable end (Fig. 1A) the foundations are extended or a few extra piers added, extra floor joists are laid, and the top plates of the side walls made longer to carry the roof over the porch area. In a true log cabin, the purlines laid across the rafters to support shingles or other roofing are also extended.

For an overhang of 5′ or so, no posts should be required unless heavy snow loads must be anticipated. It may be desirable and comparatively easy to add braces from the plates to the corner posts. The gable end of the porch roof need not be enclosed.

For a wider porch, one or even two 4-by-4 posts should be installed on each side to support the top plates, and one or more tie beams (ceiling joists) to prevent spreading of the posts and to add rigidity to the roof framing. It may be desirable to close in the gable end for the sake of appearance and to facilitate the installation of porch screening (Fig. 1D).

When the roof pitch is shallow, it's possible to extend one side of the roof to cover a porch along a side wall (Fig. 1C). For this, supporting posts should be spaced the length of the porch and no more than 4′ apart. If the roof pitch is steep, porch headroom may be too low. In this case a shed roof might be tied into the main roof (Fig. 1B), the rafters of the porch roof resting on the wall plate alongside those of the main roof. The porch roof might also be fastened to the wall as in Fig. 1F by nailing a 2-by-4 girt across the studs and supporting the porch rafters on it. In either case the lower end should rest on a top plate laid across 4-by-4 posts or 5″ logs 4′ apart.

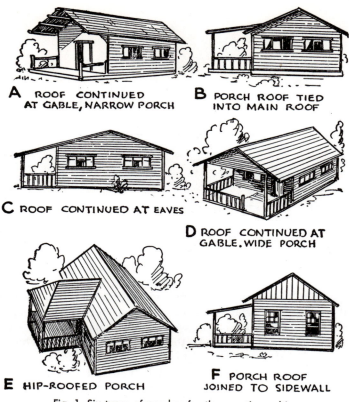

A ROOF CONTINUED AT GABLE, NARROW PORCH

B PORCH ROOF TIED INTO MAIN ROOF

C ROOF CONTINUED AT EAVES

D ROOF CONTINUED AT GABLE, WIDE PORCH

E HIP-ROOFED PORCH

F PORCH ROOF JOINED TO SIDEWALL

Fig. 1. Six types of porches for the vacation cabin.

Where snowfall is heavy, it is best to give the porch a gable or a hip roof (Fig. 1E). Its intersection with the main roof will require special care in framing and in applying roofing in the valleys where roof slopes meet.

Because they are exposed to rain, porch floors should not be level, but pitched slightly to drain away from the house. When floor joists run parallel to the house wall, a pitch of 1″ to every 6′ is readily obtained by setting each successive joist slightly lower than the last. If joists run at right angles to the house wall, the outer sill should be sufficiently lower to create the desired pitch.

Where rains are heavy or frequent, plain-edged floor boards should be used, with ⅛″ gaps between them to permit drainage. If you prefer a close-fitted floor, use tongue-and-groove redwood or cypress flooring and coat the edges with a paste of white lead and linseed oil before you lay the boards. Finish with a prime coat and two coats of good quality porch and deck enamel.

In keeping with the low modern look, some vacation homes have roofs extending over an outside terrace instead of a porch. The terrace can serve much the same purpose and requires no underpinning or floor framing, but is not as readily screened as a porch. Terraces may be built of redwood blocks, flagstones, brick, cobbles or poured concrete slabs, set into concrete or simply on a bed of sand over a gravel subsurface. Posts supporting the roof overhang may be of treated wood sunk into the ground, or heavy pipe set into concrete.

SCREENING THE CABIN PORCH. Porch railings are desirable both as a safeguard and to simplify the screening of the porch, as smaller screen panels can then be used. Solid railings can be built of siding, tempered hardboard or exterior plywood. If the railings are open, screening can be nailed on the outside. If there are no railings, screening should not be carried all the way to the floor; it is likely to be damaged by feet and chair rockers. Instead, fit 1-by-6 boards or other insect-proof material around the floor and carry screening to the top of this. In a log cabin, insect-tight railing may be made of two rows of slabs with building paper between.

Wire screening, which comes in widths to 48″, can be tacked to simple wood frames sized to fit between posts or nailed between top plates and railings. Aluminum screening is moderate in cost, requires no painting, and is not prone to rust, corrode, or cause oxidation stains.

Screen frames may be of 1-by-2 stock or the "five-quarter" lumber sometimes sold for the purpose. The 42″ width of screening will just stretch over frames built of 1-by-2 stock to fit between posts spaced 4′ center to center (the actual distance between such is about 44⅞″). Slightly wider frame stock would be preferable. If screen frames are high, one or more crosspieces should be fitted into each for greater rigidity, as properly stretched screening tends to bow in the sides.

Awnings are also desirable to keep off the sun and decrease rain exposure. Fabric awnings on spring rollers like window shades are available, as are adjustable aluminum awnings. Curtains of canvas, cotton duck or twill give fuller rain protection, but must be outside the screening to be effective. Mail-order houses such as Sears Roebuck offer roll-up curtains complete with rope, pulleys, top pole and cleat.

FINISHING OUTSIDE FRAME WALLS. If your leisure home is a frame structure, you will want to shield the floor and framing from weather as quickly as possible by covering the roof and walls. As mentioned in Chapter 8, the roof is usually covered with sheathing—boards either close spaced or with gaps, or plywood. The roofing material over this may range from tar paper to wood shingles, shakes, asphalt or asbestos roofing or shingles, tempered hardboard or plywood.

In conventional construction, the walls have an inside member (usually wallboard or plaster applied over lath), insulation between the studs (with or without a vapor barrier), outside sheathing (composition, boards, or plywood) and finally the siding, which bears the brunt of exposure to the weather. Siding may be of wood, metal or hardboard. Alternatives are stucco and brick veneer.

A vapor barrier is a membrane, such as metallic foil, through which water vapor cannot pass. It is placed on the inside of wall insulation to keep water vapor that originates inside the house (from cooking, radiant gas heating, laundering and even breathing) from penetrating the cold outer regions of the walls. Here the vapor would condense in cold weather. The resultant moisture in the walls could damage insulation, structural wood members, and paint. In the leisure home that is unoccupied during cold weather, condensation should be no problem, but it ought to be given some thought in the year-around cabin or ski lodge.

With modern materials, wall construction can be simplified and handsome effects achieved. But some of the old favorites are also worth considering.

Mill-made log siding. Applied to a frame structure, log siding simulates the true log cabin. Other materials have crowded log siding out of some dealers' stocks, but you may be able to obtain it on special order. Made of California or white pine, cedar, pecky cypress, or redwood, it consists of boards milled with a rounded face, a rabbet along one edge, and a flange at the other. These make a shiplap joint between any two boards.

If the studs and corner posts are well braced, no sheathing is required under the siding. However, plywood sheathing enables you to dispense with braces and makes for a better-insulated wall. Apply the bottom siding board first, with its bottom edge about 1″ below the sill or sheathing. Carefully level this board, and occasionally check succeeding ones. Use coated, zinc-dipped or galvanized nails.

Log siding looks most natural if boards of different widths are used. This will also enable you to bring the shadow line (joint) even with the tops and bottoms of window openings, as it should be. Try placing boards of various widths to determine which to use, before nailing any fast. Install flashing above door and window openings to lead rain runoff away. Cut ends of siding square to abut window frames.

Log siding could also be used for inside walls, so carrying the rustic motif indoors. For a cabin to be used in cold weather, this double wall might have foil-faced insulation fitted between studding.

At corners, siding can be fitted in several ways. For the mitered joint (Fig. 2), the ends must be accurately cut and both siding boards must be the same width. Square-cut siding boards may be butted against two vertical boards, one overlapping the other and both carefully plumbed, as in Fig. 3A, or fitted against a piece of square stock as in 3B. The ends of the siding may also be cut at 45 degrees and a log section nailed across them as shown at C.

Figure 4 illustrates a corner treatment more akin to actual log joints. The end of every other board is cut long to project beyond its corresponding board in the adjacent wall. If the ends are cut irregularly as with an ax, the natural log effect is heightened.

Advantages of Plywood Sheathing. Any sheathing, which is fastened directly to the studs, helps in a degree to brace the wall framing and adds some insulating value. Board sheathing—1-by-6s, 1-by-8s or even 1-by-10s—may be applied horizontally or diagonally. Composition-board sheathing has more insulating value but won't serve as a nailing base for siding or shingles. Plywood has certain advantages over both of these.

According to U.S. Forest Products Laboratory tests, a wall with no doors

Log siding is an attractive outer-wall material for a cabin in the woods. Here it has been applied vertically in front, horizontally on the sides.

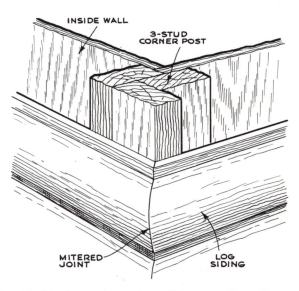

Fig. 2. Log siding finished at corners with miter joint.

or windows in it, if sheathed with ¼″ plywood panels, will be over four times as rigid and more than five times as strong as the same wall with horizontal 1-by-8 sheathing boards. A wall with one door and one window opening proved twice as rigid and almost three times as strong with ¼″ plywood nailed on as the same wall with diagonally fitted 1-by-8 boards. Because it adds such racking strength, plywood sheathing permits the builder to dispense with stud bracing (although local building codes should be checked in this regard). Plywood panels cover wall areas quickly (32 square feet at a time with standard 4′ by 8′ panels).

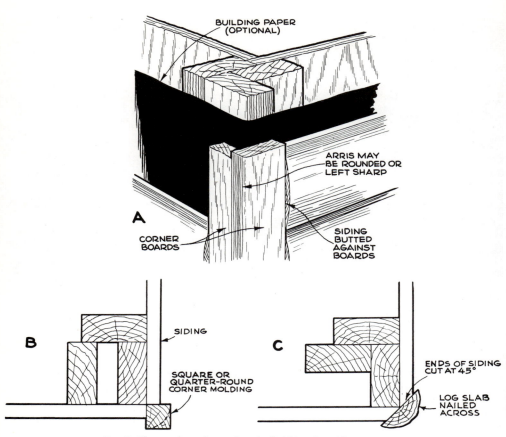

Fig. 3. Three other alternatives in finishing log-siding corners.

Although the tests mentioned were made with ¼″ plywood, standard exterior-grade sheathing comes in thicknesses from ⁵⁄₁₆″ to ¾″, the ⅜″ and ½″ panels being commonly used. They are applied with 6d common nails spaced 6″ apart along panel edges and 12″ along intermediate studs. All panel edges should be firmly backed by top plates, sole plates, or studding. If any are not, extra blocking must be nailed into the framing behind them and the plywood nailed to the blocking.

Shingling Cabin Walls. That old standby, the wood shingle, blends well into vacation backgrounds and can be stained almost any color. Shingles have slightly more insulating value than board siding, and surprisingly long life. They come in standard lengths of 16″, 18″ and 24″, and in random widths. Any shingle wider than 9″ should be split in two.

Shingles are best applied over sheathing. An alternative is to nail 1-by-3 strips horizontally across the studs (which must be braced in the absence of sheathing). But these furring strips will require door and window frames to be deeper to allow for the extra wall thickness.

Like other siding, shingles should not be put on in wet weather; the framing and sheathing should be completely dry. For longest life, shingles should be dipped in an appropriate stain before they are applied.

Fig. 4. Natural log effect can be achieved with lapped corners.

Although the bottom of the shingle line is sometimes stepped, usually shingling is done with the exposed butt ends forming even horizontal lines. Shingles in the course being laid are selected for width so that they always cover the gaps between the shingles beneath. That part of each shingle which is not covered by the one above it is called the weather exposure, and the amount permissible varies with shingle length and application. On walls the following generally holds:

16″ shingles: 6″ to 7½″ exposed to weather
18″ shingles: 7″ to 8½″   ”   ”   ”
24″ shingles: 10″ to 11½″   ”   ”   ”

Because of the shallower runoff angle, roof shingles should have 1″ less exposure than the lower of the above figures. Sometimes all shingle courses are doubled.

Like board siding, shingles are applied from the bottom up. The starting course is commonly doubled, the outer shingles being set slightly lower so that water will drip away from the foundation (Fig. 5).

Fasten shingles with zinc-coated, copper, or aluminum 3d or 4d shingle nails. Drive two into each shingle about 1″ above the exposure line so that they will be covered by the next shingle above, and slightly less than an inch from the edges. Leave a gap of about ⅛″ between shingles in the same course.

To align successive courses, a strip of wood may be leveled and tacked along the butt line, the shingles being rested on this as you nail them. Be sure to cover every gap between shingles with a shingle in the next course.

Fig. 5. Laying shingles from bottom up, lower course doubled.

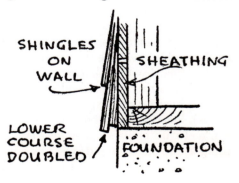

SHINGLES ON WALL

SHEATHING

LOWER COURSE DOUBLED

FOUNDATION

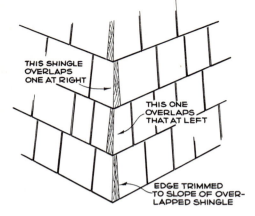

THIS SHINGLE
OVERLAPS
ONE AT RIGHT

THIS ONE
OVERLAPS
THAT AT LEFT

EDGE TRIMMED
TO SLOPE OF OVER-
LAPPED SHINGLE

Fig. 6. Shingles overlapped alternately at corners.

Select or split shingles to width as necessary to fit alongside window and door frames. Mill-made window caps have a rabbet to divert runoff; if there is no rabbet, insert sheet-metal or composition flashing. Vary shingle exposure (overlap) to make courses come even with the tops and bottoms of window and door openings.

Where walls meet, you can use corner boards as for log siding, or overlap shingles alternately in each course as in Fig. 6. Trim the end of each overlapping shingle to conform to the slope of the one that abuts it, as shown.

Shakes resemble shingles but are much longer, the standard size being 6″ by 36″. Weather exposure is proportionately greater—12″, 14″ or 16″, depending on the spacing between shakes and whether they are used on a wall or a roof. Spacing may be 1″, 2″ or 3″, these wide gaps being of course covered by the next course of shakes. Each shake is held by two rust-resistant 4d shingle nails.

Both shingles and shakes are available in a variety of synthetic materials, some of which are fireproof, and should be installed according to manufacturers' instructions.

Bevel and Drop Siding. These boards may be had in widths from 4″ to 12″. Those of ordinary bevel siding simply overlap like shingles, but weather exposure is proportionately greater, an overlap of ¾″ being sufficient for 4″ siding, 1½″ for 6″ and wider boards. As with shingles, the overlap can be varied to bring the shadow line even with window and door frames. It is of course less conspicuous if slight variations occur in several courses rather than a great difference in one.

To give the first course the same outward slant as those that follow, a starter strip is nailed at the bottom of the sheathing. This is a length of light stock roughly the same thickness as the bottom of the siding. Carefully level the first board with its bottom a little below the starter strip (Fig. 7). Nail it fast through this strip. Level all succeeding pieces, nailing them with rust-proof 8d casing nails spaced about 16″ apart horizontally. Drive only one at each location, just above the overlap, so that the boards can expand and contract with moisture changes. If siding is applied directly to studs or over composition sheathing, drive nails only at studs.

It is a good idea to paint the ends of siding boards with white-lead paint

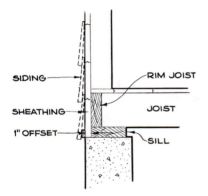

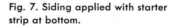

SIDING

SHEATHING

RIM JOIST

JOIST

1" OFFSET

SILL

Fig. 7. Siding applied with starter strip at bottom.

or water repellent before you put them up. Painting the entire back of each board as well is even better, provided the siding is well seasoned. If green, it is best left unpainted except at the ends. Building paper may profitably be placed behind the siding for better weathertightness, especially if no sheathing is used. Fold the paper around corners with no lap nearer than 10″. Lap vertical paper joints 6″, horizontal 4″.

If corner boards are used, they should be installed before the siding. They should be thicker than the siding and carefully plumbed to make a close butt joint with the square-cut siding boards. To make corner boards appear of equal width, the one that overlaps must be wider than the other by their thickness (Fig. 3A).

Siding must be cut to precise length to abut the corner boards. For mitered corners, which require no corner boards, each board must be cut at 45 degrees (A in Fig. 3), and unless this is skillfully done the joints will gape. Corners may also be made with boards overlapping alternately like the shingles in Fig. 6. Easiest of all are corners made. with metal plates. The board fit is undemanding and the plates are easy to apply.

Shiplap siding has a rabbet in the bottom edge that seats on the top edge of the board below. Drop siding has either a groove or a rabbet in the thick edge, which engages a tongue or a thinned flange in the next piece. Both of these sidings (Fig. 8) are more difficult to fit around openings than bevel siding because the overlap is fixed.

Like log siding, drop siding can be applied directly to well-braced studs. Facenail drop and shiplap siding with casing nails, but not through the overlap, which would be likely to split. Vertical tongue-and-groove siding can also be used. It is blind-nailed through the tongue as shown in Fig. 8.

Plywood Sidings. You can save considerable time and effort by using exterior plywood as a combination sheathing and siding. FHA requirements permit the use of ⅝″ panel siding without sheathing on studs spaced 16″, or of ½″ panel siding on studs spaced on 24″ centers. Noncorrosive nails (usually 6d) must penetrate the studding at least 1½″. A popular panel siding for this purpose, made by several manufacturers, is Texture One-Eleven.

This panel is ⅝″ thick, with square-bottomed grooves running the long way, 2″, 4″ or 8″ apart. The unsanded surface is slightly rough, and in the standard grade has small knots, checks and other natural features that blend

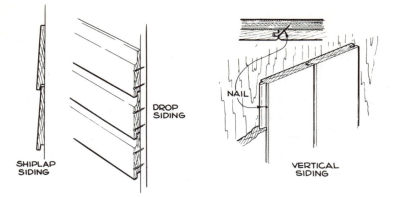

Fig. 8. Three types of siding.

into the weathered texture. A select grade panel is free of knots, patches and other face defects.

The long edges of Texture One-Eleven are shiplapped. Panels are installed with 8d casing nails driven flush but not set, 6″ apart along all edges and 12″ apart on inside studs. Neither sheathing nor stud bracing is required. The surface is easily finished with pigmented exterior stains of any color.

Other plywood sidings have V-grooves, brushed, striated and embossed surfaces, abraded grain effects, and combinations of these. Plain-surfaced plywood panels are sometimes trimmed with randomly or evenly spaced vertical wood battens, over the panel joints and between them. The battens may be painted the same color as the panel or, for some effects, a different color.

Most manufacturers offer a variety of panel sidings under their own trade names. Weldwood Weldtex for example, made by United States Plywood Corporation, has close-spaced vertical grooves of various widths that form a beautiful natural-appearing texture. Weldwood Formtex has more widely spaced, softly rounded grooves instead, whereas Weldwood Early American cedar has wide, flat grooves 12″ apart on the boldly handsome grain of Western red cedar. (This siding may be left unfinished to weather to a traditional gray patina.) All these Weldwood Duraply sidings have a resin-fiber surface that resists wear and impact, eliminates checking, and forms an excellent paint base. Some are square-edged, others form shiplap joints along the long edges.

In general, the $\frac{5}{16}$″ thickness is meant for application over sheathing; ⅜″ panels may be nailed directly to studs spaced 16″ on centers, while ½″ and thicker panels may go directly on studs at 24″ spacing. Noncorrosive casing nails should be spaced 6″ apart along the edges of square-edged panels, 4″ apart along shiplap edges, and 12″ apart along intermediate studs. The 6d size are right for siding up to ½″ thick applied over sheathing, or for ⅜″ thick siding nailed directly to studs. For ½″ and ⅝″ panel siding to go directly on studs, use 8d nails.

If any horizontal joints are necessary, they must be solidly backed with blocking set into the framing. The joint edges may be shiplapped, butted, or

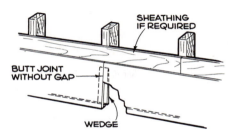

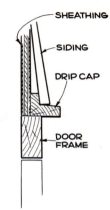

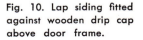

Fig. 9. Ends of plywood lap siding meet over stud, are reinforced with wedge.

Fig. 10. Lap siding fitted against wooden drip cap above door frame.

fitted with metal flashing. They should be coated with mastic or white-lead compound before installation.

Plywood Lap Siding. This gives the horizontal low-line effect so often desired in modern homes. It comes 12″ or 16″ wide and is put up much the same way as board siding, but is thinner, lighter and easier to handle. Weldwood's Duraply lap siding, for example, has the same resin-fiber surface as Duraply panel siding. The $\frac{5}{16}$″ thickness is for application over sheathing; the $\frac{3}{8}$″ thickness may go directly on studding (which must have adequate "let-in" corner bracing). With sheathing, neither bracing nor building paper is required.

A truly leveled $\frac{3}{8}$″ starter strip is nailed to the bottom of the wall under the first course only, as for wood siding. Weldwood lap siding has a factory-applied furring strip its full length along the bottom edge, which maintains the slope and creates a $\frac{3}{4}$″ deep shadow line. If laid over sheathing, the 12″ siding need overlap only 1″, the 16″ wide material 1½″. When siding is applied directly to studs, building paper should be used under it and at least 2″ of headlap is required for either width.

Over sheathing, 6d casing nails are driven through the furring strip into each stud (8d casing nails if siding is applied to studs). All end joints should come squarely over studs, and should be staggered so that those in adjacent courses are not in line. At each such joint a wedge is inserted. The two pieces of siding are butted tightly with no gap, and a nail driven through the center of each piece in addition to the usual one through the furring strip (Fig. 9).

Corners are fitted similarly to those made with wood and hardboard siding. Figure 10 shows how lap siding is fitted around door and window openings.

Weldwood Weldtex is a textured plywood lap siding. It has fine striations across the boards, which are vertical when the siding is up. In addition to the furring strip along the bottom, Weldtex has a wide rabbet along the top edge, into which the furring strip of the next piece fits. The siding is therefore self-aligning. Two widths of rabbet provide a 1½″ overlap for material to go over sheathing, or a 2″ headlap for siding directly on studs.

Hardboard Siding. Hardboard is made of wood chips expanded to open out their fibers, and then recompressed under heat and pressure. The natural lignin in them bonds the fibers firmly together into a grainless substance, denser than the original wood and equally strong in all surface directions. The front surface is very smooth, hard and dark brown in color; the back of hardboard panels usually has a screened texture.

For exterior use, hardboard is further impregnated with a special compound and baked, a treatment that improves all its physical properties. Building on this, manufacturers have produced grainless lap and panel siding that will not check or split, can be worked with ordinary woodworking tools, takes nails but resists denting and abrasion.

Masonite X-Ninety lap siding is an example of this. It comes in $\frac{7}{16}''$ thick pieces 12'' wide and 16' long, factory primed and back-sealed. It can be installed over sheathing or directly on braced studs. Building paper is recommended in either case, and a vapor barrier for structures occupied in cold weather.

A $\frac{3}{8}''$ starter strip is first nailed along the bottom of the sheathing or sill. The next course overlaps the first by 1'', nails being driven through both pieces where they overlap. Guide lines on the face side help keep courses parallel. When lengths are to be joined, they are butted *lightly* together over studs. At corners and window openings, X-Ninety is fitted much like wood siding, but a small gap is left and calking applied at butt fits. Pieces should never be sprung or forced into place.

Hardboard siding comes in panel form too. Masonite X-Ninety V-grooved siding, for example, is a $\frac{7}{16}''$ thick panel with wide V-grooves $5\frac{1}{3}''$ apart. If applied directly to studding with 6d box nails, it provides adequate racking strength and stud braces may be dispensed with.

However, all panel edges must be over studs, and the nails spaced 6'' apart along the vertical shiplap joints. They are driven into the overlapping panel so that they pass through both panels (Fig. 11), between the grooves at the top and bottom edges, and 12'' apart into intermediate studs. Over sheathing, 8d nails should be used. In V-groove siding, nails should not be driven into the grooves but $\frac{1}{2}''$ away from them. Hardboard panels should never be toenailed through the edges.

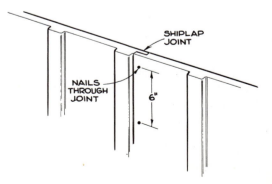

Fig. 11. Hardboard siding with molded ribs and shiplap edges.

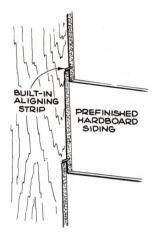

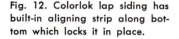

BUILT-IN ALIGNING STRIP

PREFINISHED HARDBOARD SIDING

Fig. 12. Colorlok lap siding has built-in aligning strip along bottom which locks it in place.

Panels that must be cut, and so lose their shiplap edges, may be joined by applying calking compound to the cut edges and butting them lightly together. Calking should also be used where siding is butted against trim.

Other hardboard panel sidings have square-bottomed grooves, striations, and molded ribs simulating batten boards (Fig. 11), usually with shiplap edges. Plain hardboard, such as Masonite's ⅜″ thick X-Ninety panel siding, is applied with butt joints (loosely fitted) with battens over them. It provides the same racking strength as other hardboard panels and may be applied directly to studs spaced up to 24″ on centers.

Siding with Built-in Color. A comparatively recent development is Masonite's Colorlok lap siding. This is X-Ninety siding with a tough, flexible thermoplastic film bonded to it. The polyester film, made by Goodyear Tire & Rubber Company, can be washed clean with a hose and is said to resist fading, staining, and abrasion.

Colorlok lap siding also has an angled strip set in the full length of the bottom edge at the optimum headlap distance (Fig. 12). This strip rests on the beveled top edge of the lower course, making the siding self-aligning as you install it and locking the lower edge in place without nails. At present Colorlok comes in white, green, deep tan and warm gray only.

CHAPTER TEN

FIREPLACES, HEATERS AND CHIMNEYS

A GOOD fireplace adds charm as well as comfort to a vacation home even if it is occupied chiefly in warm weather. Chilly mornings and evenings occur even in desert areas. The blight of rainy weather is much alleviated by a cheerful fire. Fireside cooking gives the barbecue chef scope for his talents, and the coziness of the hearthside is a focal point for entertainment and relaxation.

The construction of conventional fireplaces and their chimneys is demanding. Even masons who are competent in other kinds of work do not always build good ones. Close attention to the design details explained farther on in this chapter (in supervising those who do the actual work if you don't handle it yourself) is essential to building a good fireplace.

Nowadays, fortunately, you can enjoy an open fire without having a costly fireplace built or engaging in this rather difficult job yourself. Prefabricated units, comparatively easy to install, circumvent many of the problems of constructing conventional fireplaces. Many of these units blend beautifully with modern decor while retaining the age-old fascination of flickering fire-light. On the other hand, if it is simply warmth and not the fireside atmosphere you want, there are other practical ways to achieve this end.

HEATING WITHOUT A FIREPLACE. If you have power-line electricity, there are several kinds of electric heaters you can use. They are instant acting, never need fueling or servicing, and turn on or off at the snap of a switch or automatic thermostat. Unlike all flame heaters, they consume no oxygen from the air in the house, can never generate lethal carbon monoxide and require neither vent pipe nor chimney. Though their cost of operation is higher than that of gas or oil heaters, the actual difference is not likely to be large unless the leisure home is occupied in winter.

Most electric outlets are wired for a 15-ampere load and fused accordingly (some few kitchen and laundry circuits have greater capacity). A small portable heater may draw upwards of 1,000 watts, and if a few lamps and a refrigerator are powered from the same circuit, a fuse may blow whenever the refrigerator starts. Never install a fuse of greater capacity in such a case —it's a dangerous practice analogous to weighting down the safety valve of a steam boiler.

The best solution is to connect the heater to another, less heavily loaded circuit. However, where the overload is a momentary one (such as occurs when a refrigerator or pump first starts up) it is permissible to install a slow-blowing or delayed-action fuse *of the same ampere capacity*—never greater— as the normal fuse. A fuse of this kind will allow current in excess of its rating to flow for a brief time, long enough for a motor to attain its running speed for example, but it will blow if an overload persists.

The best solution of all, and the only one where large electric heaters are to be used, is a separate circuit or circuits.

Those electric heaters most suitable for use in the vacation home include the following:

Radiant Portable Heaters. Handy for quick, localized heat, these have glowing wire or ribbon elements protected by grilles. Some are the familiar bowl type, others are housed in small rectangular casings. They can be dangerous near small children, if placed too close to drapery or other combustible material, or if tipped over.

Fan-forced Radiant Heaters. A fan blows air across the hot elements in these, circulating a constant flow of warmth outward. Better portable heaters of this kind have an automatic switch that shuts them off if they are knocked over. In some, the ribbon elements are encased in glass tubes. These units may be had with automatic thermostats that switch heat on only when room temperature drops.

Radiant Wall Heaters. These fit flush into the wall and so involve no knock-over hazard. Grilles prevent contact with the hot elements. Such units are available with or without fan circulation and automatic thermostat control, in sizes of from 1,200 to 4,000 watts. They must be permanently connected to house wiring.

Baseboard Heaters. The elements of these are encased in long, channel-like housings that admit air at the bottom, heat it, and circulate it from the top. Their shape makes them inconspicuous, and because exposed parts never get too hot to touch, they are safe around tots and near furnishings. Standard lengths are 3' and 4', wattages 900 and up. They can be plugged into any suitable outlet.

Electric Steam Radiators. These need be filled with water only every week or two. A thermostat controls the heating element, and a safety valve opens at a safe preset pressure. The 1,300-watt size can be operated on a 115-volt circuit.

Heavy-duty heaters (3,000 watts and up) may have dual or triple heat ranges, the higher wattage being reserved for use in cold weather. However, units of this size should be wired to operate on 230 volts, not 115. Doubling the voltage halves the amperage for the same power.

It is possible that your wiring could provide 230 volts even though all your present equipment operates at 115. If there are two wires from the utility pole or line to your house, probably only 115-volt current is available inside. Three wires indicate 230-volt service, which in house wiring is usually split into two 115-volt legs, but an electrician can install a special heater circuit at 230 volts.

HEATING WITH BOTTLED GAS. Leaving a gas cook-stove turned on for heating is inadvisable. The flame consumes large amounts of oxygen, and the tighter the house (that is, the better your chinking, weatherstripping, storm windows and so on) the more the danger of reducing the oxygen below a safe level for the occupants.

Besides this, any flame heater may under some conditions generate carbon monoxide, the deadly gas in automobile exhausts. Whereas this and oxygen loss may present little hazard while a gas stove is used only for a limited time, as for cooking, the danger mounts when burners are left on for hours at a time, and especially if they are operated overnight.

Properly vented gas heaters dispose of these hazards. Vented heaters have a fitting to which a pipe is attached and led outdoors. This may be done through a hole in a wall—no chimney is needed. Air for combustion is taken in through the vent, and the products of combustion exhausted through it. The flame burns in a chamber hermetically sealed off from the room it heats.

Some modern gas heaters have a built-in vent that requires no pipe, but is simply pushed through a hole in an outside wall. Where vent pipes are used, they should be double-walled, with an air space between the walls to insulate hot metal from combustible house walls. Copper tubing conducts gas to the heater. Fan-circulating units, of course, require an electrical connection as well.

In addition to wall-type and console gas heaters, you can get gas furnaces to be installed under the floor between two joists. These also require a vent pipe. A long, low baseboard gas heater that projects only a few inches from the wall is vented to outer air through a 6″ by 12″ opening between two studs.

Unvented gas heaters are still available but cannot be recommended. In many localities, codes prohibit their use.

KEROSENE AND OIL HEATERS. Portable kerosene heaters are effective and cheap, but their use involves much the same hazards as do other unvented heaters, in addition to that of possible malfunction or flooding. Most kerosene heaters must be carefully leveled to insure correct feeding of the fuel. Like other portable heaters, they are not desirable where small children scurry about.

A good-sized fuel-oil heater, on the other hand, offers inexpensive warmth with reasonable safety. The simple pot burners used in many of these have no moving parts and require no electrical connection. An inexpensive model can heat four rooms but requires at least a 25′ chimney. Deluxe console oil heaters may be had with electric blowers and automatic thermostat control, but these require house current.

Fuel-oil heaters must be connected to a chimney, not merely a vent pipe. But this need not be a conventional masonry chimney. An inexpensive installation can be made with stovepipe, either double-walled or protected by a metal thimble or spacer plates where it runs through the wall, and adequately braced outside (Fig. 1). Better installations can be made with prefabricated metal chimneys as described below. Check your local code.

The oil burner must be leveled (an easy matter as most have adjustable feet for that purpose). Fuel is fed from a tank at the back of the cabinet, or through tubing and a constant level valve from an outdoor oil tank. Although a blower does not increase output, it does circulate heat more quickly and so increases a heater's efficiency.

HEATING WITH WOOD AND COAL. By installing a packaged chimney that requires no masonry work, you can burn wood or coal for heating and cooking. Mail-order catalogs still list the popular pot-bellied stove of yesteryear, as well as the venerable logwood heater—a sort of elongated cast-iron box with two removable stove lids on the top, where cooking can be done. A secondary use for stoves with enclosed combustion chambers is burning trash; they make effective if small incinerators.

For a charming Colonial atmosphere as well as utility, you can buy a reproduction of Benjamin Franklin's invention, the Franklin stove. This is a cast-iron casing with a grate inside and cast-iron doors in front of it. When the doors are closed, the unit functions as a stove or heater. Open them, and you can enjoy the glow and flickering play of an open fire. A swing-out barbecue grid adapts the unit to hearthside cookery.

Franklin stove lends an authentic touch to Colonial decor. With doors open it provides the charm of a flickering fire. *Courtesy Sears, Roebuck and Co.*

Prefabricated fireplace is easily installed by connecting it to an unused flue in an existing chimney, or to a smokepipe and special chimney, available from the manufacturer. *Courtesy Vega Industries*

Packaged as a knocked-down unit, this fireplace can be assembled with only a screwdriver. For low-cost installation in small cabins, stovepipe serves as a chimney. *Courtesy Acorn Fireplaces*

Suitable for more luxurious interiors, this fireplace comes complete with multiple-wall chimney which must extend straight up, without bends. *Courtesy Vega Industries*

You can install the Franklin stove before a fireplace, in a corner, alongside a wall or in the middle of a room. Taking their cue from it, manufacturers now offer free-standing round and rectangular open fireplace units with various attractive hood shapes. Some have big flared hoods and their own multiple-wall chimneys. The hoods themselves radiate heat and so increase the effectiveness of the open fireplace. Some units can be hung on a masonry wall.

If such fireplaces are to stand on the floor, they should rest on a fire-resistant hearthstone, a layer of brick, or ceramic tile laid in a wood frame. A combustible wall close behind any heater should be protected with a metal heat shield, which will also increase heating effectiveness by reflecting radiant heat back into the room.

STOVEPIPE AND CHIMNEYS. A properly installed vertical pipe can run straight up from a stove or fireplace unit anywhere in a room, passing through the ceiling between two joists. A flue pipe passing between two rafters then connects it to a metal chimney on the roof.

Ordinary single-wall stovepipe can be used from the heater to the ceiling; its thin wall will radiate useful heat into the room. But combustible ceiling, wall and roof members must be protected from hot stovepipes. Figure 1 shows how two pieces of sheet metal or asbestos board might be used to carry a pipe through a wall. Double-walled pipe is widely used. You can improvise it by putting one piece of 7″ smokepipe inside an 8″, and mounting both in a 9″ pipe, with rock wool or fiberglass between the two outer pipes (Fig. 2).

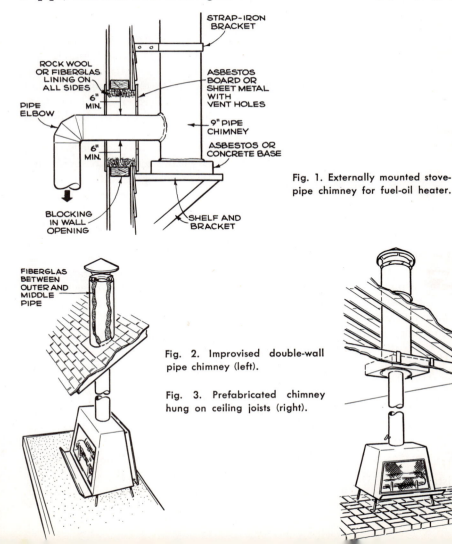

Fig. 1. Externally mounted stove-pipe chimney for fuel-oil heater.

Fig. 2. Improvised double-wall pipe chimney (left).

Fig. 3. Prefabricated chimney hung on ceiling joists (right).

Better than this is ready-made double-walled pipe with a stainless-steel flue liner and mineral insulation between this and the galvanized steel outer pipe. Makers of prefabricated fireplaces offer a full line of such pipe, including tees and elbows, with thimbles and firestop spacers (a metal shell that fits between joists to completely enclose the pipe), chimney sections, and chimney caps (Fig. 3). You can buy rectangular metal chimney housings finished like brick.

Although combustion gases are safely led outdoors through the chimney, any fireplace must draw oxygen from the inside air. Even in cold weather, therefore, it is important to leave one or more windows slightly open for ventilation, using screens or baffles if necessary to stop drafts.

Whether you put up a masonry chimney or a prefabricated one, its location is important. If it is on that side of the roof near a tree or under a downsweep of a hill, winds can set up eddy currents that force smoke back down the chimney and into the room. Putting the chimney on the other roof slope may lessen such eddy effects. They can also be counteracted in part with a chimney cap that lets smoke emerge at the sides but blocks vertical downdrafts.

A chimney should be at least 2' higher than the roof peak, or 3' higher than a flat roof; the higher the chimney, the better the draft usually is.

Where a smoke pipe enters a vertical flue at a 90-degree angle, the end of the pipe should be flush with the inner flue surface. Should it project inward, gases will be partially obstructed by the opposite wall of the flue and backdraft may result.

Pipes and flues should be cleaned out once a year at least, for leaves, soot and even birds' nests may clog them in time. An easy way to clean a chimney is to drop a rope through from the top after disconnecting the lower stovepipe, tie a straw-stuffed burlap bag to the rope and a second rope under the bag, and pull this up and down a few times.

MASONRY FIREPLACES AND CHIMNEYS. An outside masonry chimney is often attractive, requires no framing of the house structure around it, and is easier to repair, should it become necessary, than an inside chimney. It can serve a fireplace indoors and a barbecue outdoors, perhaps facing a patio. An inside chimney may serve fireplaces in adjacent rooms, or a living-room fireplace and a kitchen range.

A masonry chimney must be built on a substantial foundation reaching below the frost line. Skimping on the foundation is poor economy, for settling due to insufficient support, or heaving as the ground beneath freezes, may crack the entire structure. The chimney foundation should be planned with that of the house, but should be separate from it. No part of a fireplace or chimney should be supported by the house framing. Chimney and fireplace should be a self-standing unit, and should in fact logically be built before the rest of the structure.

The excavation for the fireplace foundation should be well below the frost line, with the bottom corners square. A footing at least 12" thick should first be cast, preferably with metal reinforcing in it. Foundation walls may next be built up of concrete blocks set up with suitable mortar in the form of an open box, or cast 8″ thick. A form built so that it can be collapsed for removal is lowered onto the footing inside the excavation and the concrete walls are poured around it.

When the form has been removed, the inner cavity is filled with stone, sand and gravel—not soil—and tamped down hard. Another reinforced concrete slab, several inches thick, is then cast over it and the walls. Heavy fence wire, steel or iron rod, or even an old iron gate may be set in for reinforcement. Fire brick, laid up with fire clay instead of ordinary mortar, is then laid over the slab to form the hearth.

You now have a choice between building a conventional fireplace or constructing a masonry shell around any of several prefabricated steel units. These embody all the requisites of correct fireplace design. In addition, one model has double walls through which air passes and is returned to the room, making it a far more efficient heating device than the old-fashioned fireplace.

Should you choose the old-fashioned type, an understanding of its parts is important. They are the fireplace opening, the throat, the smoke chamber, and the flue. The shapes and proportions of these must follow fairly rigid rules if the fireplace is to perform satisfactorily.

The opening should be wider than it is high, never higher than it is wide. A width of 30″ is minimum for easy tending and the burning of half-length cordwood. The height of the opening should be at least 28″; if this is increased, the width should be somewhat greater than 30″. A piece of angle iron is usually set in at the top of the opening to support the masonry above.

The fireplace cavity should taper back sharply from the opening as shown in Fig. 4. To better reflect heat forward into the room, the back of the fireplace should slope forward at the top as shown. Its upper corner should be 8″ above the top of the opening. This forms the throat, which should extend the full width of the fireplace. Usually 4″ to 5″ wide, the throat has in it an iron frame that carries the damper mechanism.

Only above the throat, and not before, should the sidewalls of the fireplace start to taper in toward the flue. A slope of 12″ in 18″ of height is recommended for easy passage of the hot gases. This tapering cavity is the smoke chamber. Its vital functions are to funnel the gases into the flue, provide a space in which downdrafts will be slowed and diffused, and temporarily hold smoke blown back down the chimney by erratic wind gusts. Without a smoke chamber, these would be blown back directly into the room.

The horizontal surface formed on top of the fireplace back, called the smoke shelf also plays an important role and should not be omitted. It turns downdrafts back upon themselves, giving them an upward movement as they enter the smoke chamber, from which they are returned up the chimney by ascending flue gases.

The inner front surface of the smoke chamber should taper gently like the sidewalls. All the inside surfaces of the smoke chamber and shelf should be coated with smoothly troweled cement plaster, at least ½″ thick, to reduce friction and promote the flow of gases.

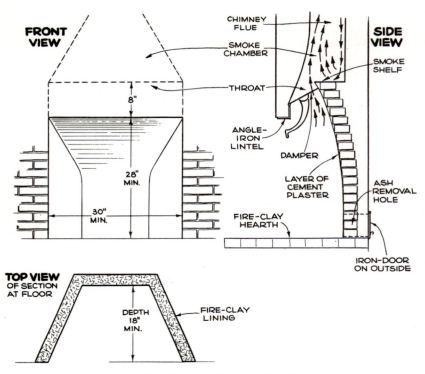

FRONT VIEW

SIDE VIEW

CHIMNEY FLUE

SMOKE CHAMBER

THROAT

8"

SMOKE SHELF

ANGLE-IRON LINTEL

DAMPER

28" MIN.

30" MIN.

LAYER OF CEMENT PLASTER

ASH REMOVAL HOLE

FIRE-CLAY HEARTH

IRON-DOOR ON OUTSIDE

TOP VIEW OF SECTION AT FLOOR

DEPTH 18" MIN.

FIRE-CLAY LINING

Fig. 4. Plan of a typical masonry fireplace

At the top, the smoke chamber tapers to the size of the flue, or chimney passage. A round flue should have a cross-sectional area of at least one tenth that of the fireplace opening; a square flue should be slightly larger. As a cross check, see that there are 15 to 16 square inches of flue area for every square foot of fireplace opening.

Flues should not taper to a smaller size, nor have sharp setbacks or steps, but remain the same size and run as straight as possible to the top of the chimney. If offsets or turns are unavoidable, they should be gradual and without constrictions.

A flue must be lined with smooth, fire-resisting material. The simplest way to do this is to use commercial flue lining, available in various sizes and shapes. It is set in place as the chimney rises, and filled around with cement. The round form offers less resistance to spirally moving gases and can be cleaned more easily than square or oblong flues. Local codes may specify what size and type of lining must be used, and how flues must be spaced if there are two in a chimney. There should be at least 4" of masonry on all sides of the flue.

The chimney must be absolutely plumb and stand clear of all other parts of the structure by at least 2". Rock wool or other fireproof material is usually packed into this gap. To test a chimney for leaks, build a fire of leaves or tar paper in the fireplace and cover the top of the chimney with a board or a wet blanket. Escaping smoke will mark any leaks, which should be carefully plugged with mortar. The joint between roof and chimney should be bridged with copper flashing.

Fireplace construction is too complex to be recommended to the inexperienced builder. It is considerably simplified with a prefabricated circulating or noncirculating unit such as those made by Heatilator. These are steel forms that become part of the fireplace structure. They have all the critical elements built in and provide a supporting core around which a masonry facade of almost any kind can be built.

The instructions provided with the unit must be carefully followed. The masonry is not set up directly against the Heatilator form; asbestos insulation is first packed around it to shield the masonry from excessive heat and to permit free expansion of the metal. For the circulating model the masonry must be chambered and fitted with grilles to let cold air in at the bottom and warm air out at the top.

MODERN OPEN-SIDED FIREPLACES. Comparatively new are fireplaces open on two, three or even four sides. Such a fireplace can be built into a chimney corner, at one end or inside a masonry room divider, or under a central chimney, the hood being supported by four columns.

There is a prefabricated unit that simplifies this kind of construction too. Made by Heatilator, the Universal Damper is a four-sided tapering hood or smoke dome with a built-in damper. Its sturdy flanged edges form supporting lintels for the masonry above it. Except in the four-sides-open version, the masonry completely encloses the dome. As Fig. 5 shows, insulation is packed between the metal and the masonry, and the chimney should be built with a smoke shelf, which serves the same purpose as its counterpart in conventional fireplaces.

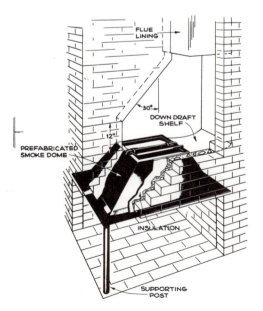

Fig. 5. Plan of an open-sided fireplace made by Heatilator.

CHAPTER ELEVEN

FINISHING THE INTERIOR OF YOUR CABIN

OCCUPANCY OF a vacation home often begins as soon as the outside walls are up and minimum utilities provided. The fishing or hunting lodge may require no more. Cabin walls of real logs, or even those made of split logs, may be left as they are if the structure is to be occupied only in mild weather. The rustic appearance of whole logs is difficult to improve upon.

If the inside walls are flat log sections, insulating value and greater weathertightness can be gained by installing roofing paper, felt or other insulation, and interior paneling. Many people will wish to do this to conceal the crudity of bare slabs or open studding. Before covering any wall, however, make certain that all pipes, wiring, switch, fixture and outlet boxes are in place. If access to the inside wall may occasionally be necessary, frame an opening in the wall paneling that can be closed by a removable cover.

A classic wall treatment consists of vertical boards of uniform or random width. Common square-edge boards can be nailed to blocking or furring strips as described further on, and the joints covered with battens or else beveled slightly so that a groove is formed between boards.

MILL MADE BOARD PANELING. This is made of knotty pine, ponderosa pine, pecky cypress, redwood, cedar, fir, hemlock and other woods. Usually of nominal 1″ thickness, the boards have tongue-and-groove edges, come in several widths (6″, 8″ and 10″) and may have plain or molded (shaped) faces.

Whether you use common boards or mill-made boards, you must toenail horizontal blocking between the studs, flush with their inside edges, at heights of 2′, 4′ and 6′. Vertical boards can then be nailed to blocking, top and sole plates (Fig. 1).

However, if the studs are not reasonably true, furring strips should be applied instead as in Fig. 2. Fit thin wedges or shims behind them wherever a warped or poorly plumbed stud is behind the overall plane of the wall. Also nail vertical pieces of furring to the studs between the horizontal furring to make a flush nailing surface there. Try to make board joints over studs whenever possible; in between, nail the boards to the furring.

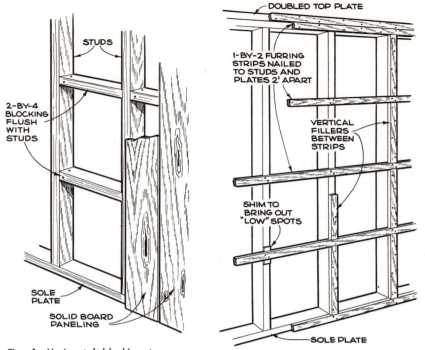

Fig. 1. Horizontal blocking toe-nailed between studs.

Fig. 2. Furring strips nailed to studs.

Blind-nail tongue-and-groove boards with finishing nails driven through the tongue. When the grooved edge of the next board is fitted, no nails will show. Board paneling can profitably be finished before you install it. This insures getting even tones all over (if a board finishes differently, it can be matched to like ones or relegated to an inconspicuous place). It is also easier to finish the tongued and grooved edges this way, whereas they may show skips if the finishing is done after the boards are up.

PANELS THAT SIMULATE BOARDS. Instead of boards, you can buy standard-sized plywood panels with a face veneer of knotty pine, birch, cypress, walnut, cherry and a host of other fine woods. These are generally grooved to look like boards, and it is difficult to tell the difference. The panels cover big wall areas quickly, and the thicker ($7/16''$) variety require no furring strips or blocking if the studs are true. Some manufacturers offer prefinished panels of this kind that can save you much tedious hand finishing.

TEXTURED PLYWOOD WALLS. Fir plywood is glamorized either by disguising its characteristic wild grain or by capitalizing on it. Closely spaced grooves produce interesting striated or combed effects. Sandblasting or wire brushing abrades part of the grain, leaving harder sections in bold relief, to produce driftwood and sculptured effects. The bas-relief of such surfaces can yield unusual two-tone effects if a base coat of one color is applied and wiped off the high spots, to which another color is applied afterwards.

HARDBOARD WALL PANELING. Besides plain hardboard panels (which may be the standard grade for interior use), you can get hardboard with V-grooves, U-grooves, deep or shallow striations, simulated tile and leather surfaces, and perforations, the latter being small holes either 1″ apart or in patterns. The perforations accommodate wire hangers to hold anything from garden tools to bric-a-brac. Other hardboards (such as Masonite Seadrift) have the dramatic bas-relief effect of sandblasted wood grain molded into their splinter-free surfaces. Intriguing modern effects are possible with these materials.

In the deluxe range are hardboards with simulated wood-grain surfaces. Masonite Royalcote comes in three kinds of cherry and walnut, besides elm, teak, pecan and oak. The grain and color are permanently bonded to the surface, requiring no finishing and practically no maintenance; the panels can be wiped clean of soil and stains, and waxed if you wish.

INSTALLING PLYWOOD PANELING. Before applying any kind of paneling, it is recommended that the panels be laid flat, with spacers between to let air circulate on both sides, in the room where they are to go. After two or three days they will reach the same moisture content as the framing, and relative movement after installation will be minimized. (For hardboard panels that have dried out in the sun or that are to be installed in damp locations, be sure to follow the manufacturer's conditioning instructions.)

Neither hardboard nor plywood panels should be forced into tight contact at joints; if they are, future expansion may cause bulging or loosening.

The thinner (¼″) plywood paneling is best applied over ⁵⁄₁₆″ or ⅜″ interior plywood sheathing, which should run horizontally, at right angles to the paneling or over furring strips. These may be 1-by-2s or 1½″-wide strips of ⅜″ plywood, nailed to the studs horizontally 24″ apart as for board paneling (Fig. 2). Stud surfaces should be brought out flush with the horizontal furring at least every 48″ (where panel joints will come) by nailing on like pieces as shown.

Heavier (⁷⁄₁₆″ thick) paneling may be nailed directly to studs if they are reasonably true; if not, furring should be applied first and shimmed level.

Each panel should be prefitted to its position, and notches or necessary openings cut out before it is fastened. Figure 3 shows how to scribe an edge that is to fit against an irregular contour. Measure or scribe cuts to fit panels around door and window openings. Cut panels to a length that will leave ¼″ of clearance at the floor or ceiling.

In cutting with a hand saw or on a table saw, place the "good" face of a plywood panel (the one that will show when it is installed) facing up so that cutting splinters will be on the back. With a portable power saw or on a radial-arm saw, both of which cut upward, the good face should be down.

Stand the first sheet in a corner, with its other long edge centered over a stud, and plumb it carefully on this edge. Use the nails and nail spacing specified by the manufacturer. Remember to provide solid backing (with blocking if need be) at all panel edges. Nails driven through grooves virtually disappear, but if necessary, nails can be set and puttied over.

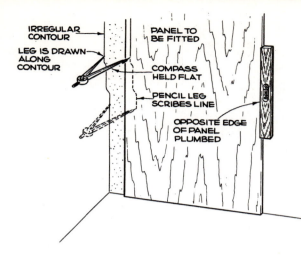

IRREGULAR CONTOUR
LEG IS DRAWN ALONG CONTOUR
PANEL TO BE FITTED
COMPASS HELD FLAT
PENCIL LEG SCRIBES LINE
OPPOSITE EDGE OF PANEL PLUMBED

Fig. 3. Scribing an edge to fit an irregular contour.

An even more rigid wall is achieved by brushing glue (any reasonably slow-setting glue) on the studs or furring strips before nailing on the panels. Nails can be spaced farther apart. Edges can be tack-held by driving nails only partly; after the glue has set, they are pulled out before trim is applied.

Panels can also be installed with contact cement, no nails being used, but the method holds pitfalls for the beginner. One or two coats of contact cement are applied to studs or furring and to those areas of the panel back which will touch them. After the cement has dried for the time specified by the maker, the panel is set partially in place, one long edge against the room corner or the edge of the previously applied panel. When correctly so aligned, it is swung into position against the backing (the cement will seize instantly) and the cemented areas are pounded with a padded mallet. Once in contact, panels cannot be shifted.

For nailing hardwood plywood paneling, you can obtain special nails in colors to match the grained surfaces; they need only be driven flush. To avoid marring the panel surface, drive nails within ⅛″ of it and finish with a nail set or punch. Ordinary noncolored nails may be set $\frac{1}{16}$″ deep and concealed with matching putty.

Concealing Joints and Fitting Trim. Most fine paneling is designed to make unobtrusive or even decorative joints by itself. Where plainer paneling is used, or material must be cut and joined at other than shiplapped edges, the simple methods shown in Fig. 4 are applicable. In addition, various strip moldings (some of metal but with wood-veneer facing) are available to conceal joints and corners. If plywood edges must be chamfered, this is best done with sandpaper folded around a block; planing tends to tear ply edges unless the blade is very sharp.

At outside corners, paneling can be mitered, but it is easier to conceal corner joints with special trim or common wood molding. For inside corners, one panel is fitted close to the corner post and the other butted against it. If an irregular corner line introduces gaps, the second panel can be scribed to fit or a strip of quarter-round molding applied.

Along ceiling lines, a waste strip of paneling may be used as in Fig. 5.

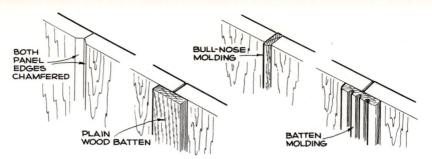

Fig. 4. Four methods of concealing joints at panel edges.

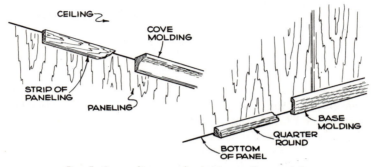

Fig. 5. Concealing panel edges at ceiling and floor.

Other possibilities are quarter-round, or cove molding, as shown. The simplest baseboard treatment is a strip of quarter-round; plain 1-by-3 stock or a base molding can also be used.

If door and window jambs are the correct width (which will vary according to what backing, if any, is used behind paneling), the paneling can simply abut them. The gap between them is then covered with ordinary casing trim (Fig. 6A) or plain, neatly fitted boards. If sheathing or furring strips bring the paneling out beyond the jamb edges, add a filler strip of appropriate thickness (Fig. 6B). If casing has already been applied over sheathing or wallboard (Fig. 6C) the paneling may abut it, with a bead molding set into the joint.

INSTALLING HARDBOARD PANELS. Standard, tempered or prefinished hardboard panels ³⁄₁₆″ or thicker may be applied directly to studs that are spaced 16″; the ⁵⁄₁₆″ thickness can be used on studs spaced 24″ on centers. Hardboard only ⅛″ thick must be applied over a solid backing. All panel edges must have firm support, from blocking if necessary.

As in cutting plywood, saw hardboard with the good surface where the blade enters. Fit panels so that all joints will be free, never tightly butted. There should always be a small gap between hardboard panels.

Hardboard can be installed with nails, screws, glue and nails, or contact cement. Nails are most commonly used. Space 4d finishing nails (or special hardboard nails in colors to match prefinished surfaces) 4″ apart around the edges and 8″ inside the body of the panel. Drive these inside nails first,

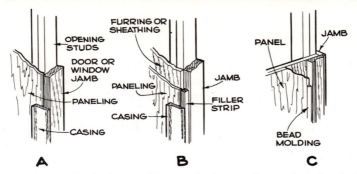

Fig. 6. Three methods of concealing panel edges at door and window jambs.

fastening the edges last. Always nail perpendicular to the surface and at least ⅜" from the edge; never toenail hardboard. If you wish to set casing or finishing nails below the surface, predrill small holes for the heads first.

The problems of fitting hardboard at corners, concealing joints, and installing trim are the same as with other paneling. Matching moldings for Masonite's prefinished simulated-grain paneling are available.

BUILDING PARTITION WALLS. Load-bearing partitions that help support the roof or stair openings must be framed as substantially as walls. But partitions that carry no structural load, or the light walls often needed to enclose closet areas or divide rooms, can be framed with 2-by-2s, 2-by-3s, or 2-by-4s placed flat to the wall line. The sole plate must be of 2" nominal width. Such thinner walls save space and, provided framing is spaced on 16" or 24" centers, can be paneled with the same material as other walls.

CEILINGS AND SOFFITS. Informal cabins and small A-frame structures are sometimes left without ceilings. In hot weather, warm air can rise to the roof peak (and out, if gable louvers are provided) with some gain in personal comfort. But conversely the ceilingless house is harder to heat in cold weather, and its room partitions afford only partial privacy at best.

Ceilings are best installed before wall paneling. Tile board, acoustic or plain, need only be stapled to furring strips nailed across the joists according to the maker's directions. Plywood, fiberboard, and hardboard are also likely ceiling materials. Among the hardboards, Masonite's ¼" Panelwood (which is somewhat less dense than the standard panel), standard or tempered Presdwood, Ridgegroove and Ridgeline siding make attractive ceilings.

These ¼" and thicker panels can be nailed directly to ceiling joists (tie beams) or against sheathing. Framing members should be no more than 16" apart, and each panel edge should bear against a framing member. Where panel joints occur at right angles to the joists, nail headers (blocking) between the joists. Nail hardboard ceiling panels with 5d (1¾" long) box, siding or sinker nails 6" apart within the panels, 4" apart along all edges. Butt joints may be covered with molding or battens.

A T-shaped support will be of great help in holding up ceiling panels. It should be about ½" longer than the distance from floor to ceiling joists, with a crossbar 4' long. If a strip of lath or other light stock is temporarily nailed to the wall studs about ½" below the joists, one end of a panel can be inserted there, the panel lifted with the support, and the latter gradually straightened up until it stands of itself.

Soffits are horizontal panels—in effect, ceilings—enclosing roof overhangs or eaves. Plywood or exterior hardboard is often used for these. Both require framing that will support all panel edges.

Where the eaves overhang is 16" or less, the fascia board (a 1-by-6 or similar board nailed across the plumb cut at the end of the rafters) may be grooved to receive the panel (Fig. 7). Alternatively, 1" stock may be nailed inside the fascia board, the paneling nailed to this, and a strip of molding added below. At the house wall, a 2-by-2 nailed to sheathing or studding serves as a nailing base. The siding may then be fitted up close under the soffit as shown.

For wider soffits, breezeway or porch ceilings, framing members on 16" centers should be nailed between the top plates, or between the wall and the fascia board as shown in Fig. 8. Under these nail 1-by-2 stringers at right angles to the framing and no more than 16" apart. Nail filler pieces between the stringers wherever panels end or join.

STEPS AND STAIRS. A few flat stones embedded in sand or gravel may

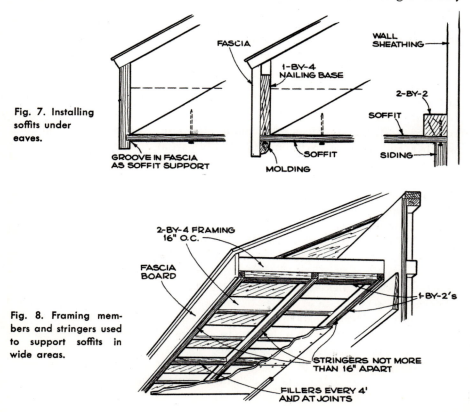

Fig. 7. Installing soffits under eaves.

FASCIA

1-BY-4 NAILING BASE

WALL SHEATHING

2-BY-2

SOFFIT

SIDING

GROOVE IN FASCIA AS SOFFIT SUPPORT

SOFFIT

MOLDING

Fig. 8. Framing members and stringers used to support soffits in wide areas.

2-BY-4 FRAMING 16" O.C.

FASCIA BOARD

1-BY-2's

STRINGERS NOT MORE THAN 16" APART

FILLERS EVERY 4' AND AT JOINTS

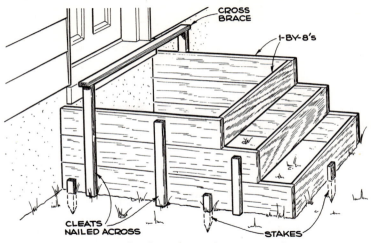

Fig. 9. Wooden forms for casting concrete steps.

suffice for the approach to a low porch or door sill. Stepping stones laid to form a walk up to the door may be doubled to form shallow steps; these should be set in mortar. Concrete blocks, too, may be laid stair-wise on a gravel or concrete foundation, the latter below frost line for permanence. Outdoor steps can also be cast of concrete in wooden forms open at the tops of the treads (Fig. 9). Use a stiff concrete mix that won't overflow the form. If railings are to be installed, you may want to set in the mounting bolts while the concrete is soft.

Wooden outdoor stairs may be built on piers or concrete blocks (Fig. 10)· with stair blocks nailed to 2-by-4 stringers as shown. Tread width can be so proportioned that the triangles cut from a 2-by-6 are all the same size, so that there is no waste except at the ends of the stock. Treads are best made of two or three boards gapped to let rainwater drain out. No actual risers are needed, the front of the steps being left open.

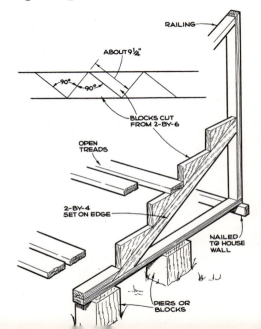

Fig. 10. Wooden stairs built on piers.

CHAPTER TWELVE

MODERN UTILITIES FOR THE VACATION HOME

SUCH PROSAIC things as a water supply and means of lighting, heating, cooking and waste disposal are as essential to leisure living as a roof over your head. They should be given serious consideration even before the land is bought, for if commercial utilities are not available you must be prepared to supply your own or reasonable substitutes.

For a brief stay at a hunting or fishing cabin, it's possible to carry water by the bucket. This won't serve the vacationing family that requires far more water—for drinking, cooking, dishwashing, laundry, bathing and lavatory use. But whether you carry it in a pail or pipe it in through an automatic pump, the first essential is a source of good water.

In vacation areas it is rarely possible to connect to a municipal water supply. If it can be done, this is of course a simple solution. Sometimes a group of vacationers can share in developing a mutual water supply, which of course has the advantage of dividing the cost among several.

You may even be offered free water from a friendly neighbor's source. But even good neighbors may come to disagree in time, or the other owner may sell out to less friendly folk. Your only certain protection, if you depend on such an arrangement, is to have it in the form of a written agreement. This should include an easement for the pipe that carries the water across the other property to yours, and the agreement should be legally recorded.

No matter what the source of the water, or how long other people have been drinking it, you should have it tested by a local or state health laboratory before using any of it unboiled. Such testing is done free or for a nominal sum; the authority involved usually supplies a sterile bottle to be filled. Even clear, sparkling water may have a high bacteria count, animal parasites, or their eggs. Don't rely on verbal assurances, appearance, or taste to judge the safety of drinking water. Local people are sometimes unaffected by water that tests show to be of questionable purity.

If there are encrustations or signs of salt-like deposits at the source, it's wise to have the water tested for mineral deposits. Water with an excessive mineral content may be unsuitable on this count alone.

It should be pointed out that water softeners do not remove minerals from hard water, but only alter their reaction with soap so that satisfactory lather can be obtained. Only an ion-exchange demineralizer can actually remove excessive minerals in solution.

EVALUATING A WATER SOURCE. A pond or lake or other stagnant source cannot be recommended. A running brook in sparsely settled country is better, though always liable to pollution. Even if tests show the water of a stream to be acceptable today, septic-tank drainage, accident, or future construction may contaminate it at a later time. Water from very shallow wells is equally susceptible; either excessive rainfall or drouth may reverse the normal flow of ground water to carry pollution where it would not otherwise go. It is even possible in this way for contaminating drainage to reach a water source on what appears to be higher ground but in terms of subterranean flow is not.

A spring may supply you with good water if it is properly tested, evaluated and developed. Find out first whether it flows all year long; local folk may be able to tell you. If you can inspect the spring at the end of a dry summer and find it flowing, it will probably be dependable the year around.

Have the water tested. If it proves pure, the next question is whether its flow is adequate at all times. A spring that gushes in spring but subsides to a trickle in summer is not worth your time or money. One that flows at a modest but fairly constant rate, on the other hand, may serve. Its development will require a storage tank, from which water can be drawn faster than it flows from the source. Even so, the water in the tank must be replenished in each 24-hour period for practical purposes.

For all purposes, including bathing, each person needs about 50 gallons of water per day. If the undeveloped spring *reliably* delivers half a gallon per minute (720 gallons per day) it can provide water for an average family —but none for the irrigation of shrubbery or a garden. In dry areas of the West, even a small garden can consume 1,200 gallons or more every day. As for swimming pools, they are best forgotten unless there is a truly abundant supply of water; a small pool holds upwards of 10,000 gallons.

HOW TO DEVELOP A SPRING. Though it's possible to diminish or even block off the flow of a spring by faulty development, it isn't possible to boost the flow. Sometimes, however, it is feasible to hook up two or three springs to a common storage tank and so form an adequate supply.

The next step is to safeguard the spring from pollution by rain runoff, insects, animals and decaying matter. This means enclosing the source and taking water out through a pipe. Where the spring bubbles up out of the ground, one method is to excavate and sink two or more lengths of concrete pipe around it, the top piece with a T-connection for the delivery pipe and another a few inches higher as an overflow. The pipe should extend above ground as a curbing to keep out soil runoff, and should be covered on top, preferably with a concrete slab.

If spring seepage comes up over a large area, such a pipe may block off

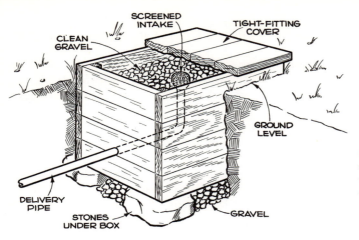

Fig. 1. Trapping spring seepage with wooden box sunk in excavation.

part of the source simply because the pipe isn't big enough. In such case you can build a bottomless cypress or redwood box of adequate size, excavate to a depth of 4' or more, spread a layer of stones over the bottom, and set the box on this, installing a delivery pipe with a screened intake. The box is then filled with clean gravel and a securely fitting lid installed on it (Fig. 1).

A spring in a hillside is not so easily enclosed. If the flow comes from several places, see whether it is possible to channel them together. Sometimes it is possible to dam up and so divert the flow before it is lost. If there is a hillside shelf where the water appears, you may be able to dig a deep hole or trench at the site, drive a delivery pipe in from the side, and put a concrete cover on top (Fig. 2). Even better is an excavation lined with brick or concrete, with a gravel bottom to let the flow enter.

Where there is no shelf, it may be feasible to dig a horizontal tunnel back into the hill, shoring it if necessary (a potentially dangerous job unless you are accustomed to this sort of work). The front opening should be dammed up to hold water, with a screened opening above it big enough to enter for cleaning when necessary.

Where water issues freely from rock in a single adequate flow, tampering with the rock may diffuse or lessen the supply. It's safest to channel it into a catch box (by cementing a metal or wooden trough into place, for example). Embed the delivery pipe (with a screened inlet) in coarse gravel at the bottom of the box. Mount a cover, leaving it open only where the water enters. This opening can be screened.

Ideally the storage tank should be below the spring but above the house.

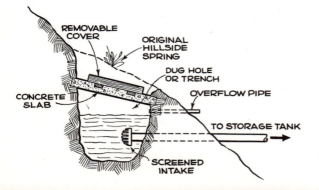

Fig. 2. Hillside spring trapped in trench and piped off.

Water will thus flow by gravity alone; a difference of 65' to 100' in height between the tank and the house will provide a respectable pressure head at the faucets, no pump being necessary. A metal storage tank should be shaded unless you're content with sun-heated water. Wooden tanks transmit less heat to the water, and if made of redwood require no painting. Tank capacity should be at least a day's consumption; more is better.

BRINGING IN A WELL. In some areas, especially in the Southwest, trying to bring in a well is very much of a gamble. Even where well water is abundant, its quality may render a well useless. Local experience, the existence of successful wells nearby, and the counsel of well diggers and drillers familiar with the area are valuable though by no means infallible guides. It should be noted that the existence of persistently damp spots may be only a seepage of ground water and not a likely location for a well. The value of water witches or dowsers is highly controversial, but if there is one with a good record of well strikes you may do better to consult him rather than probe for a well with only your own guesswork to guide you.

Wells can be dug, driven, or drilled. Two or three men can dig a shallow well (20' to 30' deep) in a few days with the aid of a tripod tower and block and tackle to haul out excavated material. Care must be exercised to avoid cave-ins. In some soils it's safer to start the hole larger than desired and let it taper smaller toward the bottom. It may be necessary to brace the walls with timbers as digging proceeds. In wet, unstable soil it's safer and quicker to excavate with a centrifugal pump—flushing away the soil with a stream of water and then pumping water and soil out. This method has the advantage that a wood, metal or concrete casing can be forced down as the hole deepens.

However it's dug, the well should be lined with redwood, bricks, concrete blocks, concrete or vitrified sewer pipe. Big pipe is one of the best well linings. Each section is placed with the socket end up, and joints are cemented. There should be a base of stone or gravel at the bottom to let water in, with sand on top of it. If the pipe is carried a little above ground, it will keep out dirt and soil water.

A concrete platform or cover, several inches thick, with a manhole in it for cleaning, should be cemented on top of the lining. Never enter a well to clean it unless you first lower a lighted candle into it. If the candle goes out, ventilate the well for several hours, and check it again before going down.

Shallow dug wells often yield water for decades, but they are always subject to pollution through seepage or ground runoff. Never dig a shallow well nearer than 100' to any source of possible contamination. Have the water tested at regular intervals and, as an added precaution, any time there is a prolonged wet or dry spell.

A driven well is brought in by driving a pipe down until it strikes water. In loose soils without rocks, wells have been driven as deep as 100' by hand with a sledge hammer or a weight raised by tackle and repeatedly dropped. Additional sections are screwed on to the top end of the pipe as previous ones are driven down, extra-strong couplings being used to withstand the driving shocks. At the bottom of the first length is a well point—a sharp-ended fitting with screened holes for water to enter.

Driving a well is an inexpensive method but hard work. In most soils well points cannot be driven much beyond 25', and any rock formation will block progress entirely. Should the pipe be bent or deformed against a stone, it may be impossible to feed lift- or jet-pump fittings past that point. Often the pipe strikes dense soil layers it cannot penetrate to reach good water just below. And finally, although they often deliver water for years, well points usually become clogged in time.

Open-end driven wells are less subject to this. As the pipe is driven, soil enters the open end but is constantly removed, either by a sand pump or by flushing with water forced down a smaller pipe inside the other. Either hand or gasoline-powered pumps can be used.

It's easier and safer, though more costly, to have a professional drill your well. He can tap water from strata 100' down or more, where it is far less liable to pollution, although it may have a high mineral content. Again, the experience of local people is your most likely guide.

Well drilling is expensive—$4 or $5 per foot, including the casing. Make inquiries about the driller, and take the trouble to speak to any customers he gives as references. A driller may or may not give you an estimate of the depth to which he will have to drill (and charge you for). But if he does, remember that mere verbal assurances have no legal weight. Lacking written guarantees, you can be charged for a dry hole, though a reputable driller will not try for a well where he thinks success unlikely. When he does strike water, he will usually pump the well for a time to establish its rate of flow, which is useful information when you're shopping for a pump.

BRINGING WATER TO THE HOUSE. A spring-fed storage tank involves no machinery, noise, or power supply. But a well requires at least a pump. The simplest is a hand-operated suction pump mounted on the well head or, if the distance is not great, on the kitchen sink. Since atmospheric pressure is what raises the water, a suction pump can work only to a depth of about 22'. A lift pump, with its cylinder in the casing, can raise water from 50' down. Below that, you need a deep-well pump. Some of these have the pumping unit in the well, but the popular jet pump's mechanism is all above ground. Only pipes and a jet head extend to the water level below.

A storage tank isn't usually necessary with a well provided the well's flow is adequate, but a tank may be used to provide pressure at the faucets. Such a system costs more than a simple pressure tank, which is often part of the pump equipment. The tank holds only a small amount of water; an automatic switch runs the pump, which forces water in while compressing air in the tank above it. When air pressure reaches a preset limit, pumping ceases. Water can then be drawn from the tank under the pressure of the entrapped air, the pump cutting in again only when air pressure drops to a certain minimum.

Where electric power isn't available, you may have to settle for a storage tank and a gasoline-powered pump, running this for a few hours every day to build up a water reserve for the 24-hour period. If there is no site on high ground for the tank, it will require a tower, at additional expense.

A less familiar pumping system, requiring no outside power at all but applicable only where there is an abundance of flowing water, is a hydraulic ram. The only moving parts in this are automatic valves. A heavy surge of water flows through until it shuts one valve, whereupon the inertia or momentum of the water forces some of it uphill past a delivery valve. When the driving force is gone, this valve closes, the main one opens, and the action is repeated. As such an installation requires expert planning, some masonry work and a storage tank, first cost is not low.

Some houses have been built with roof gutters that route all rainwater into a cistern or tank (sometimes built under the house porch). As rainfall cannot be regulated, the tank must be very large to carry enough reserve for dry spells—20,000 gallons is not uncommon. The only expense with such a system is the cost of running an automatic pump to drive the water upstairs, and the softness of rainwater is desirable for household use. But obviously the system is practical only where rainfall is fairly heavy and dependable, and the cistern must be safeguarded from insects, rodents and dirt.

HEATING HOUSEHOLD WATER. Electric water heaters are made small enough to fit under a sink, but are practical only where power comes from commercial mains or from a large private plant. Gas water heaters can be operated from bottled gas (propane, butane, or LPG), which is convenient for heating, cooking and even lighting besides.

In sunny climes, some success is claimed for solar water heaters. These are usually a grid of pipes built into a box, with a glass cover over it, oriented to face the sun during most of the day. The pipes and interior of the box are painted black to absorb a maximum of heat. A well-insulated storage tank may be installed *above* such a heater to hold a reserve of hot water, circulation between tank and heater taking place due to the difference of temperature. Obviously sunless days will leave the water cold, and in view of its cost such a "free" system may not be as good a buy as an electric or gas water heater.

In the absence of both gas and electricity, hot water may be obtained from a tank and an old-fashioned "pot stove," which has a jacket through which the water circulates and can be fired with any solid fuel, coal being the most practical.

COOKING, LIGHTING, AND REFRIGERATION. Lacking electricity, you can manage nicely with bottled gas. The large tanks hooked up outside the house provide service just like city gas, and at reasonable cost. Stoves work the same way as on commercial gas, but should be purchased for use on LPG as the orifices and air adjustment are different.

Bottled gas can also fuel a water heater and room heaters, and perform the reverse function of refrigeration. However, gas refrigerators are relatively more expensive than electric ones, and they require a vent to the outdoors for safety.

Where house-trailer supplies are sold, you may be able to buy mantle gas lights for mounting on walls, thus solving a lighting problem as well.

Kerosene cook stoves, despite their venerable age, are a practical solution where bottled gas is not available. A properly operated, clean kerosene burner gives a hot, clean flame with no oil odor. Kerosene is a safer fuel than gasoline for this and other purposes. Check with your insurance agent to make sure your policy recognizes your right to use kerosene, gasoline, or bottled-gas appliances.

Gasoline mantle lanterns give a surprisingly bright light (equivalent approximately to a 100-watt bulb) at low cost, burning for about twelve hours on a quart of leaded or unleaded fuel. But they hiss in operation, must be pumped up occasionally, and involve an inherently dangerous fuel. Their more modern equivalent is the propane lantern, which has a miniature flask of pressurized gas. It requires no priming or pumping, but costs more to operate than the gasoline type.

YOUR OWN ELECTRIC POWER PLANT. With a 115-volt alternating-current generating plant, you can use the familiar genies of the modern household—refrigerator, fluorescent and other lights, television, vacuum cleaner, and power tools. In fact, if you plan to buy a power plant, you should do so before you build so that you can use it to operate an electric drill, sabre saw, circular saw and sander when you need them most.

However, only a very powerful generating plant could handle all the appliances you take for granted at home, where a commercial network shoulders the load. There are severe limitations on the number of things you can operate from the average private lighting plant at one time. An additional consideration is the fact that it must be running whenever electricity is to be used.

Older outfits charged banks of storage batteries, from which power could be drawn even when the engine was not running. But these have given way completely to alternating-current plants, which are simpler, cheaper, and require far less maintenance. The A.C. generator has no troublesome commutator, but only two or three collector rings and brushes, with appropriate suppression circuits to avoid radio and TV interference. In some generators the magnetic field rotates inside stationary generating coils, so that only a small exciting current instead of the output current passes through the brushes. Generators are now commonly direct-coupled to the engine, doing away with belts, chains and gears.

Plants are available with either two- or four-cycle engines. Both are satisfactory, but two-cycle engines require oil to be mixed with the gasoline. Four-cycle engines have crankcase lubrication, like most cars, and they can be outfitted to run on natural or LP gas instead of gasoline, so eliminating the fueling chore entirely.

The specifications of one leading power plant state that its two-cycle engine will deliver 1,500 watts for 2½ hours on a gallon of fuel. A larger generator of the same make with a four-cycle engine will furnish 3,000 watts for 1¾ hours on a gallon of gas.

Selecting Plant Capacity. Electric power (watts) is the product of voltage or electrical pressure, and amperage or volume of electrical flow. Current-using equipment may be rated directly in watts (as light bulbs are) or in amperes at a stated voltage. Simply multiply these two figures to convert to watts.

Lamps and heating appliances draw their rated wattage at all times. But motors complicate load evaluation because they draw far more current at starting than once they are running. A split-phase motor that runs on 400 watts, for example, may momentarily draw over 2,000 on starting. This abnormal load must be considered in choosing a power plant. Some manufacturers rate theirs at both a constant-duty and a surge output, the latter wattage one the plant can sustain only for a brief time.

Next to motors (especially those driving refrigerators, pumps and air conditioners) the heaviest current users are heating appliances, from toasters and percolators to room heaters. Some of these would require the entire output of a small lighting plant. It is not practical to think of running an electric range or any but the smallest water heater from a private plant.

To estimate your electrical power needs, add the wattage of all light bulbs to be used, plus the starting wattage of all automatic motor-using units such as water pumps and refrigerators. Finally, add 25 percent for reserve power. The total wattage is a conservative minimum rating for the power plant. Common plant ratings are 1,000, 1,500, 2,500, 3,000 and 3,500 watts. Some generators deliver current at 230 volts, with so many watts available from each of two 115-volt legs.

Canny use can stretch plant capacity somewhat. For example, if generator output is equal to the running load of one unit and the starting load of a second, it may be feasible to first start the one that is to run steadily, and only then plug in the automatic or self-starting unit. Or, if several motors must be run at once, you might start the one that takes the heaviest starting current first, then cut in successively smaller ones as each settles down to running. It must be pointed out that the horsepower rating alone offers no complete guide to starting demands; the kind of motor is equally important. A repulsion-induction motor draws only about one third as much starting current as a split-phase motor of the same horsepower.

If you buy a generating plant only for emergency use in case commercial power fails, the same rating considerations apply. You might reduce the generator load, and so get by with a smaller outfit, by disconnecting air conditioners and heating appliances while the emergency lasts. For such stand-by service, your plant must be connected to the house wiring through a manual transfer switch that simultaneously cuts your wiring off from the outside power line. This keeps current from your generator from entering the outside line and vice versa, and is vital not only to prevent damage to your equipment but to protect linemen at work restoring commercial power.

Most lighting plants are started by hand, with a rope or a recoil starter. They can also be had with push-button electric starting, for which a special circuit keeps a storage battery charged. Fully automatic plants start themselves up on demand—that is, whenever a light switch is snapped on or a refrigerator or other automatic unit calls for current.

Wiring your vacation home is equally critical whether it is to draw current from a private plant or from a power line. All wiring and equipment should conform to the National Electrical Code and pertinent local codes. Usually a permit must be obtained before wiring is begun, and an inspection passed when it is completed. Some local codes permit wiring to be done only by licensed electricians.

GARBAGE AND SEWAGE DISPOSAL. Unless there is a regular collection of garbage it must either be burned or buried a safe distance from the water supply. Even dishwater should not be thrown out where it may seep into the well or other water source. A kitchen drain should preferably run to a dry well or a covered pit, to which a little chloride of lime (bleaching powder) is added from time to time. The dry well is simply a lined hole in the ground, with a stone or gravel bottom to promote seepage out of it, and a lid on top so that soil won't clog it. It can be built of a barrel, an oil drum, or a length of large-diameter concrete or vitrified sewer pipe.

Under no circumstances should such a dry well, a privy or a septic tank be near a shallow well. Even locating such a waste-disposal system downhill from a well is no guarantee against contamination for the water table below ground is horizontal. In some cases subterranean water even flows uphill through fissures in soil strata.

The drain line from a sink may be of 4″ vitrified tile, with well-cemented joints. Instead of emptying into a dry well, the line may be closed at the end, the last few tile being laid with open joints in an 18″ deep bed of coke, coarse sand, gravel, slag or cinders. This may be covered with tar paper and a 12″ depth of soil.

Septic Tank Systems. If water is piped to the house, both sewage and kitchen drainage can be disposed of through a septic tank. The tank itself does not get rid of this material; it is merely a holding chamber in which the waste is broken down into a more fluid form by bacterial action. Eventually it passes out of the tank into a distribution field where it disperses into the ground.

In claylike soil, or where there is solid rock under a shallow depth of soil, the effluent from a septic tank will not penetrate the ground but remain near the surface. Besides constituting a malodorous nuisance, it may be washed by rain and groundwater flow into streams and wells and so become a serious health menace. A similar situation may prevail where the water table is so high that the septic-tank overflow cannot sink in. Under such conditions, installation of a septic tank is not advisable. An outside privy located where it cannot contaminate the water supply is actually a safer, more sanitary solution.

Where To Write For Plans and Information

American Geodesic, Inc.
One Merchant's Plaza
Bangor, Maine 04401

Boyne Falls Log Homes
Boyne Falls, Michigan 49713

Cluster Shed, Inc.
Hartland, Vermont 05048

Hart & Cooley Manufacturing Company
Division of Allied Thermal Corporation
Holland, Michigan 49423
(Chimneys)

Heatilator
Division of Vega Industries
Mt. Pleasant, Iowa 52641
(Fireplaces)

Home Building Plan Service
2235 N. E. Sandy Boulevard
Portland, Oregon 97232

International Homes of Cedar
P. O. Box 268
Woodinville, Washington 98072

The Majestic Company
Huntington, Indiana 46750
(Fireplaces)

Masonite Corporation
29 North Wacker Drive
Chicago, Illinois 60606

Ward Cabin Company
P. O. Box 72
Houlton, Maine 04730

Western Wood Products Association
Yeon Building
Portland, Oregon 97204

INDEX

A

A-frames, 14, 23, 32–33, 114–116, 145
All-in-One Connecticut cottage, 34–35
Anchor bolts, 63, 64, 95, 96
Anchors, framing, 100
Awnings, 119

B

Bald cypress logs, 80
Balloon framing, 98, 99, 104
Batter boards, 60, 61, 97
Beams, built-up, 97
Birch (veneer), 141
Black & Decker Co., 54
Breezeway, 14
Bridging, 102, 103
Budget-priced dream house, 24–25
Building codes, 95
Building lines, laying out, 60–62
Bull, Fredrik, 32
Bureau of Land Management, 20

C

California cabin, 30–31
California pine, 120
Calking, 91–92
Cantilever deck, 115
Cedar board paneling, 140
Cedar log siding, 120
Cedar logs, 80
Ceilings, installation of, 145, 146
Chain saw, 53
Character loans, 21
Chimney, double-wall, 135, 136
Chimney, masonry, 136, 137
Chimney, prefab, 135, 136
Chimney, stovepipe, 135
Chinking, 91–92
Chisels, 46
Choosing a site, 18
Circular saw, 48–49, 53, 56
Cluster Shed, 26–27
Concrete, 68–70
Contact cement, 143
Coping saw, 45
Copper naphthenate, 62–63
Corner posts, 105
Creosote, 63, 95
Crosscut saw, 45
Cypress, 95
Cypress (veneer), 141

D

Deep-well pump, 152
Double header joists, 101
Double trimmer joists, 101
Door openings, 107, 108, 116
Doubling plate, 10
Douglas Fir Plywood Association, 25, 33, 37, 40, 44
Drill, battery, 54–55
Drill, electric, 49–50
Drill, hand, 46–47

F

Fascia board, 75, 146
Federal Register, 20
Financing a vacation home, 20–22
Finish, Linseed oil, 92
Finish, Logwood oil, 92
Finish, varnish, 92
Finish, wood-seal, 92
Fir board paneling, 140
Fireplace, framing for, 101
Fireplaces, masonry, 136, 137
Fireplaces, open-sided, 139
Fireplaces, prefabricated, 134
Fir logs, 80
Flue, 137, 138
Footings, 65, 66, 67
Forest Products Laboratory, 81, 82
Foundation, expansion, 59
Foundation, how to build, 60–70
Foundation, location of, 57
Foundation, pier, 62–64, 96
Foundation, slab, 66–68, 113
Foundation, walls, 65–66, 95–96, 136
Framing, floor and ceiling openings, 101
Framing, roof, 109–112
Framing square, 99, 102, 109, 110, 111
Framing, wall openings, 107, 108, 116
Franklin stove, 133, 134
Free land, 19

G

Gable roof, 89, 109–112, 118
Gable roof, geometry, 110
Gable roof, laying out, 110–112
Garbage disposal, 156

Generators, 154, 155
Girders, 96, 97, 100
Grout, 95, 96

H

Hand tools, 45–46
Hammer, 46
Hardboard, 127, 128, 142
Header, continuous, 106, 107
Heaters, baseboard, 131
Heaters, bottled gas, 132
Heaters, electric, 131, 132
Heaters, fan-forced radiant, 131
Heaters, kerosene, 132
Heaters, oil, 133
Heaters, radiant portable, 131
Heaters, radiant wall, 131
Heaters, solar water, 153
Heaters, water, 153
Heatilator, 139
Hemlock board paneling, 140
Hip roof, 90, 109, 118
Homarina boathouse, 40
Home Building Plan Service, 157

I

Interiors, finishing, 140–147

J

Joists, ceiling, 109
Joists, floor, 83, 84, 98, 99, 100
Joists, header, 101

K

Kentucky Lake, Kentucky, 19
Keyhole saw, 45
Knotty pine, 140, 141

L

Lanterns, gasoline, 154
Larch logs, 80
Leasing land, 19–20
Level, 45
Lift pump, 152
Lighting, 152–153
Loans, leisure-home, 21
Lodgepole pine cabin, 41
Log Buildings, 40–44
Log cabin, 79–94
Log cabin, corner joints, 85–87, 92
Log cabin, finish, 92
Log cabin, foundation, 82
Log cabin, framing, 87–89
Log cabin, planning, 82–83
Log cabin, pre-cut, 80
Log cabin, roof, 89–90
Log cabin, sills, 83–85

Log cabin, walls, 83–85
Log construction, dovetail corner, 92
Log construction, groove-and-tenon
    corner, 92
Log construction, round-notch corner,
    85–86
Log construction, tenon corner, 92
Logs, peeled, 81, 82
Logs, unpeeled, 81

M

Masonite Colorlok, siding, 128
Masonite Corporation, 29, 71
Masonite Panelgroove, 75, 76
Masonite Panelwood, 145
Masonite Presdwood, 75, 77, 145
Masonite Ridgegroove, 145
Masonite Ridgeline, 145
Masonite Royalcote, 28, 142
Masonite Seadrift, 142
Masonite X-Ninety V-groove, 29, 128

N

National Association of Home Builders, 14

O

Octagonal houses, 24–25, 36–37
Oklahoma State University of Agriculture
    and Applied Science, 91
Omega dome, 30–31

P

Palisade log walls, 93
Paneling, concealing edges of, 144
Paneling, mill-made board, 140, 141
Paneling, wall, 140–146
Panelized construction, 113, 114
Pecky cypress, 120, 140
Pentachlorophenol, 62, 72
Pier blocks, 97
Pine logs, 80
Pitch, 109, 110, 117, 118
Platform framing, 97, 104
Plumb line, 45
Plywood, 104, 113, 120, 121, 125, 141, 142
Pole cabin, 71–78
Ponderosa pine, 140
Porches, 117–119
Porch floors, 118
Portland Cement Association, 69
"Pot stove", 153
Pumps, 152, 153

R

Radiators, electric steam, 131
Rafters, erecting, 112, 113
Rafters, laying out, 109–112

Railings, porch, 119
Ranch for All Seasons, 38–39
Redwood, 80, 95, 120, 140
Refrigerators, 153
Ridge piece, 112
Right-angled frame, 60
Ripsaw, 45
Roof, covering, 90–91
Roof, sheathing, 113
Roofing, roll, 113
Run, 109, 110

S

Sabre saw, 50–51
Sander, belt, 52
Sander, orbital, 51
Sander, straight-line, 51
Sanders, 51–52
Sawed joists, 84–85
Sawhorses, 46
Screening, porch, 119
Screwdriver, 46
Sears Roebuck Co., 119
Septic tanks, 156
Sewage disposal, 156
Shakes, 90, 124
Sheathing, board, 120
Sheathing, plywood, 113, 120, 121, 125
Shed roof, 109, 111, 112
Shingles, 90, 122, 123, 124
Siding, bevel, 124, 125
Siding, drop, 124, 125
Siding, hardboard, 75, 127, 128
Siding, log, 120, 121, 122
Siding, panel, 76, 116
Siding, panelgroove, 76
Siding, plywood, 125, 126, 127
Siding, shiplap, 125
Skil Corporation, 54
Smoke chamber, 137, 138
Soffits, 145, 146
Southampton 28 vacation house, 42
Span, 109, 110
Split logs, 94
Spring, how to develop, 149–151
Stairs, stone, 146, 147
Stairs, wooden outdoor, 147
Steel square, *see* Framing square
Stoves, kerosene, 154
Subfloor, laying, 104
Suction pump, 152

T

Table saw, 48
Techbuilt, Inc., 42
Template, 99, 100
Tennessee Valley Authority, 19
Terraces, 118
Texture One-Eleven, 125

Textured plywood, 141
Tools, battery-powered, 54–55
Tools, electric, 48–52
Tools, extension, 56
Tools, gas-powered, 52–53, 55
Tools, hand, 45–47
Tools, portable, 48
Tools, shock hazard, 55
Trimmers, 108
Trusses, prefabricated, 113
T-sill construction, 98, 99
Two-story Pole Cabin, 28–29

U

Udall, Stewart L., 20
Underpinning, pier, 96–97
Underpinning, post, 96–97
Underwriters' Laboratories, 48
Universal Damper fireplace, 139
U. S. Department of Agriculture, 66
U. S. Forest Service, 19, 81, 82, 85, 88, 91, 109
U. S. Plywood Corp., 126

V

Vacation home, financing, 20–22
Vacation home, location, 16–17
Vacation home, materials, 21, 22, 24
Vega Industries, 134
Veneer-faced plywood, 141

W

Walls, assembling, 104–105
Walls, bracing, 106
Walls, concrete, 65
Walls, fieldstone, 65
Walls, outside finishing, 119–129
Walls, partition, 96, 100, 145
Walls, raising, 105
Walls, stone, 66
Walnut (veneer), 141
Water, bringing to house, 152
Water, developing a spring, 149
Water, evaluating purity, 149
Water, heating, 153
Water level, 60, 61
Waterside homes, 23, 36, 40, 42, 43
Weldwood Duraply, 126, 127
Weldwood Early American cedar, 126
Weldwood Formex, 126
Weldwood Weldtex, 126, 127
Wells, how to dig, 151, 152
White pine, 120
Window openings, 107, 108, 116
Wooden pier foundation, 62–64
Wood preservatives, 62–63